CANCELED SCIENCE

CANCELED SCIENCE

WHAT SOME ATHEISTS DON'T WANT YOU TO SEE

ERIC HEDIN

SEATTLE   DISCOVERY INSTITUTE PRESS   2021

Description

Eric Hedin was enjoying a productive career as a physics professor at Ball State University when the letter from a militant atheist arrived and all hell broke loose. The conflict spilled first onto the pages of the local newspaper, and then into the national news. The atheist attack included threats from the Freedom from Religion Foundation, which targeted Hedin after learning his Boundaries of Science course exposed students to an evidence-based case for design and purpose in cosmology, physics, and biochemistry. *Canceled Science* tells the dramatic story of the atheist campaign to cancel Hedin's course, reveals the evidence the atheists tried to bury, and explores discoveries that have revolutionized our understanding of the nature and origin of matter, space, and even time itself.

Copyright Notice

Library Cataloging Data

Canceled Science: What Some Atheists Don't Want You to See by Eric Hedin.

252 pages, 6 x 9 x 0.5 & 0.75 lb, 229 x 152 x 13 mm & 0.34 kg

Library of Congress Control Number: 2021931751

ISBN-978-1-63712-000-2 (paperback), 978-1-63712-001-9 (EPUB), 978-1-63712-002-6 (Kindle)

BISAC: SCI015000 SCIENCE / Space Science / Cosmology

BISAC: SCI075000 SCIENCE / Philosophy & Social Aspects

BISAC: SCI027000 SCIENCE / Life Sciences / Evolution

BISAC: SCI005000 SCIENCE / Physics / Astrophysics

BISAC: SCI098010 SCIENCE / Space Science / Planetary

Publisher Information

Discovery Institute Press, 208 Columbia Street, Seattle, WA 98104

Internet: http://www.discoveryinstitutepress.com/

Published in the United States of America on acid-free paper.

First Edition, First Printing, March 2021.

Dedication

In memory of David Ober (1939–2017), professor and
former chair of the Department of Physics and Astronomy
at Ball State University. Colleague, mentor, and friend.

CONTENTS

1. The Boundaries of Science

"The science of cosmology may be suggesting that science itself provides reasons for doubting scientific naturalism."
Rodney D. Holder[1]

I DIDN'T GO INTO PHYSICS AND ASTRONOMY TO END UP IN THE MIDdle of a national media controversy. Seeking the limelight was never my passion. My career interest began with reflection and a love of nature.

I was eighteen years old, and having awakened in the middle of the night, I stepped out of the stone and sun-bleached timber shelter at Camp Muir on the east slope of Mount Rainier. I was at 10,000 feet elevation, and the cold air and a silent breeze from across the glacier quickly replaced my drowsiness with keen excitement. And then I looked up.

The night sky was awash in a wake of brilliant stars, so many that they seemed to blend together into a jeweled blanket of light. The Milky Way streaked across the dome of the heavens like the exultant stroke of a masterful artist. Uncountable in their profusion, the myriad stars in this heavenly panorama made me feel at once awestruck and exhilarated, as if in that moment I had been invited to join in the cast of an ancient celestial drama.

Experiences like this one on our family's climb up Mount Rainier fostered in me a deep love and appreciation of nature. I was blessed to grow up in the Pacific Northwest, where unspoiled nature, both ocean and mountains, lay close to home. My father was also an avid outdoorsman, and even when I was very young my life was filled with camping and hiking in the beautiful outdoors of Washington State.

I also enjoyed reading science fiction stories. Their far-flung settings and plots engaged a longing in me. Even in junior high, however, I began to think that I needed to read some real science books so that my understanding of the natural world would become more grounded in reality. An astronomy book on quasars fascinated me, as did another that explained Einstein's theory of special relativity.

My decision to major in physics in college hardly needed any deliberation. I really didn't know then what to do with such a degree, and in the science building at Seattle Pacific University one day I was startled to hear my physics professor nonchalantly say, "When you go to graduate school…" I had never considered such a thing, but given how much I enjoyed physics, it began to make sense.

I went on to earn a PhD from the University of Washington for my study and research on experimental plasma physics. Having completed about twenty-four years of schooling by that point, I reasoned that the last thing I wanted to was work in academia. My dream job came through when I received an invitation to serve as a guest researcher at the Royal Institute of Technology in Stockholm, Sweden.

Both of my grandfathers had immigrated to the States from Sweden in the early nineteen hundreds, and so an opportunity to work and live in "the old country," as my grandmother called it, felt almost too good to be true. I got a chance to work alongside some terrific people on experimental fusion energy research, became fluent in Swedish, met more relatives there than I ever knew back home, and made great friends within an international community.

It was a good experience, but along the way I began to sense that my life could have a greater and more lasting impact through teaching than in pure research. That desire eventually led to me to a tenure-track faculty position in physics and astronomy at Ball State, a public university in Indiana. The institution is named after a manufacturer of glass canning jars—a benign backstory for an utterly benign university campus.

Or so I imagined.

Science and the Big Questions

I HADN'T been at Ball State long before I discovered that my astronomy students were fascinated by modern discoveries in physics related to the origin and fine tuning of the universe, and by questions raised by those discoveries, questions concerning purpose and the meaning of life. So I approached the chair of the Department of Physics and Astronomy, a seasoned physicist with decades of teaching and research experience, and asked him about the possibility of developing a course that explored these questions alongside astronomy and cosmology.

He suggested the Honors College would be the appropriate place to introduce a course at the interface of science and human concern. So, I drafted a course proposal with a course description that read as follows: "In this course, we will examine the nature of the physical and the living world with the goal of increasing our appreciation of the scope, wonder, and complexity of physical reality. We will also investigate physical reality and the boundaries of science for any hidden wisdom within this reality which may illuminate the central questions of the purpose of our existence and the meaning of life."

I titled it "The Boundaries of Science."

The next step was to meet with the dean of the Honors College. We were ushered into a quiet conference room with a long, polished wooden table, the top of which must have been four inches thick. The dean came in and sat on the opposite side. I don't remember much of the conversation, which mostly took place between the dean and my department chair. The dean probably said something about needing to respect students' widely differing views on faith and religion, and I assured him that I'd do that and let the evidence of science speak for itself.

One of the goals of the Ball State Honors College for their Symposium in the Physical Sciences courses was to promote critical thinking about the societal implications of science and scientific discoveries. And since that was what I had in mind, the course was a good fit. The dean quickly greenlighted it, and I was off and running.

The class rooted its inquiry and content in science, with the primary subject matter involving an overview of classical and modern physics and an introduction to cosmology, stellar life cycles, and planetary formation. This allowed the students to appreciate how the laws of nature have acted to produce the backdrop, stage, and props necessary for our own existence.

Pushing religion was never on the agenda, but neither did I quash discussion of topics based on scientific evidence with religious implications. My goal was to give a presentation of well-accepted and mainstream scientific evidence and theories, and let the students explore the larger implications.

I would write a question on the board and a lively discussion would ensue. The students came from a variety of backgrounds with respect to their levels of scientific literacy and views on religion. Most of the time the class taught itself as the students offered insights and challenged each other with follow-up questions.

These discussions confirmed my earlier impressions that many of the deepest concerns of my students at Ball State related to questions about the meaning of life in general, and their own significance in particular.

Some scientists insist that the twentieth-century discovery of how vast the universe is demonstrates that Earth and humanity are insignificant compared to the cosmos. This outlook often makes it into high school and university science courses, giving students the impression that science drains the meaning and significance from human experience and affirms a philosophical outlook known as nihilism.

Some public scientists and science professors enthusiastically promote this interpretation of the scientific evidence. But not every scientist is especially thrilled by this. "Science, and particularly the narrowly focused and reductionist science of the present day, is perceived as denying the world meaning," writes distinguished cell biologist Franklin Harold, "and without meaning humans cannot live."[2]

Is the nihilistic perspective unhealthy, as Harold suggests? A good question. But there is a more fundamental question: Is nihilism actually supported by the scientific evidence? As we will see, there are world-class scientists on both sides of this issue. Where did my Boundaries course land? Rather than pushing nihilism, I encouraged my students to evaluate the broad range of scientific evidence related to our significance and come to their own conclusions.

In the semesters that followed, the course was reviewed positively by both the dean and the associate dean of the Honors College, my student evaluations were consistently good, and demand for the course remained brisk.

After six years of teaching it, there was another happy development. Ball State decided to hire a brilliant young scientist to join the faculty, an astrobiologist I had a lot of respect for and who had co-authored a book that touched on some of the very issues raised in my Boundaries course. It looked like smooth sailing ahead for me at Ball State.

My rude awakening came in the spring of 2013.

The Letter

ASTRONOMER AND astrobiologist Guillermo Gonzalez had just been hired to join our department. At the meeting to announce this, the chair of the faculty search committee said Dr. Gonzalez had previously been a tenure-track faculty member at Iowa State University. He also added that Gonzalez had been railroaded out by a group of aggressive atheists who objected to a book he'd co-authored, titled *The Privileged Planet*. I was familiar with the book, in which astronomical, cosmological, and geological evidence was presented that pointed towards the purposive design of Earth and its place in the cosmos.

I left the meeting and headed back to my office feeling encouraged. Gonzalez had an impressive body of academic publications for his age; his work on galactic habitable zones had even been featured on the cover of *Scientific American*.[3] I was excited to have him on board. Back in my office I sat down at my paper-cluttered desk and opened my email. The first thing I saw was a forwarded note from the department chair.

The email contained disturbing news about my Boundaries of Science course. Jerry Coyne, a nationally known atheist, blogger, and evolutionary biologist, had acquired a copy of my class syllabus and asked my chair to verify if it was being used in a science class at Ball State. Dr. Coyne opined that the course amounted to teaching a "religiously infused science course" at a public university and violated the separation of church and state.[4] On his view, the course was simply "religion served under the guise of science."

I couldn't believe that anyone could accuse me of violating the First Amendment with my teaching, and I was later pleased to learn that even some of Coyne's fellow atheists found his tactics repugnant. As commentator David Klinghoffer noted:

> Even Coyne's fellow atheist bloggers PZ Myers and Laurence Moran are troubled by the implication that it's appropriate to try to strike with the weapon of the law at a professor at another university whose views you don't like.
>
> Moran, a biochemist at the University of Toronto, has been surprisingly good on this. As he notes, there's something really offensively weasel-like about going after Eric Hedin by complaining to his employer. You want to criticize Dr. Hedin's ideas on your blog or in some other appropriate medium? Sure, definitely. Go for it. But try to get him punished or reined in by his supervisors? That's contemptible. Writes Moran, "I ban people from *Sandwalk* [his blog] if I ever hear of them trying to intimidate someone by complaining to their employer. That's unacceptable behavior in my book."[5]

I was none too happy to be under attack, of course. And yet, as concerned as I was, I really had no idea what I was in for in the months to come. That day in April 2013 marked the beginning of an escalating dispute, one that would spark a national media firestorm.

At the heart of the controversy was the thesis that some things we find in the universe require more than a purely material cause, a view held by many philosophers and scientists down through the ages and into the present. In my course I exposed my students to some of these thinkers, along with some on the opposite side of the question. But for Coyne, that was too much. Naturalism holds that nature is all there is, and that the order of the universe, including the order of the living world, is merely the result of the laws of nature, or, as some put it, of "chance and necessity." Coyne went a step further. He insisted that this view cannot even be questioned in a public university science course—or to be more precise, cannot be questioned even in a cross-disciplinary course on scientific discoveries and their larger cultural implications.

But the question as to whether philosophical naturalism is true is too important to shove into a corner. This and other closely related questions are precisely those anyone striving to live an examined life will ask, and I encouraged my Boundaries students to ask those questions in the light of modern discoveries in astronomy and physics.

We will explore such questions in these pages. They include: Are matter and the laws of matter all there is? Do the things we have discovered about physical reality undermine or support a conclusion of human significance? When we experience a sense of wonder in contemplating the vastness of our universe, what if anything does that feeling signify? If we feel small and lost as we contemplate the vast reaches of the universe, what if anything does that tell us? Is either emotional response informative? How do we fit into the overall scheme of things? Is life meaningful, or meaningless? Can science shed light on what we might most earnestly desire to know? What are the implications of the fact that our universe is not eternal, but had a beginning? Why is there something rather than nothing? What about intelligent design (ID), the idea that certain features of the natural world are best explained by reference to an intelligent cause rather than to any purely mindless material cause? And going beyond that hypothesis, can science provide support not just for intelligent design but for the existence of God?

Those were some of the questions that my interdisciplinary course posed, and Coyne made clear that he didn't like it one bit. After his initial accusatory email, he took his case against me onto his blog, where his overripe rhetoric was lapped up by the media like yellowjackets gorging on a rotten apple. Soon the Freedom from Religion Foundation, a group of militant atheists based in another state, launched a media attack against me, insisting that my presenting scientific evidence in the Boundaries course in support of human significance was tantamount to establishing a state-sponsored religion.

From here rumors spread quickly through the internet, and I became the target of numerous email attacks from other zealous atheists.

One said, "You should be ashamed of yourself, pushing that nonsense onto impressionable young minds." My razor-sharp Honors College students would have taken issue with being described as "impressionable young minds." Also, I am soft-spoken and non-domineering by nature, and if any pushing of religious viewpoints occurred in class, it didn't come from me. I feel that most people would not like to have anything foisted on them, including atheism.

The attack emails were only the beginning. Before long, the media got wind of the story, and more than a few news reporters played along with the atheist hit pieces in their attempts to sensationalize the story. If some atheist who didn't know me and who had no firsthand knowledge about my course said on a personal blog that I was "proselytizing" in my class, newspapers would report that I had been accused of pushing religion down my students' throats.

Throughout the media storm, I was repeatedly amazed at how misinformed the news reports were. One such instance came from the *Star Press*, the local newspaper there in Muncie, Indiana. As Evolution News noted, the *Star Press* article made it sound as if I had required students to read numerous pro-ID articles as part of a mandatory reading list. In fact, the "reading list" was actually just a bibliography of some resources relevant to the class, and was not part of any assigned reading. Muffing that distinction was just the tip of the misinformation iceberg. Evolution News explained at length:

By transforming Hedin's "Partial Bibliography" into an assigned "reading list," the *Star Press* article misleads readers about the list's importance and misrepresents the content of Hedin's course. But the unfairness of the article goes deeper than that: If the reporter was going to discuss Hedin's "Partial Bibliography" fairly, he should have noted that it includes writings that attack both intelligent design and creationism, such as Francis Collins's *The Language of God*, which devotes an entire chapter to bashing intelligent design in biology. The bibliography also includes writings by scholars who hold a variety of religious positions. Physicist Roger Penrose is an atheist. The late philosopher Antony Flew was an atheist-turned-deist. Physicist Paul Davies is perhaps best described as a pantheist. The authors represented by the "Partial Bibliography" are much more diverse than the critics of Hedin have claimed.

The *Star Press* article does eventually discuss one of the two books that are genuinely assigned to be read in Hedin's course, *God's Undertaker* by John Lennox. However, the second book required by Hedin isn't even identified, let alone discussed. That second book is a straight science text, *The Expanding Universe: A Beginner's Guide to the Big Bang and Beyond*, by Mark A. Garlick. Of course, discussing Garlick's book wouldn't fit the caricature being offered by critics of Hedin's course either.

The article's discussion of the book by John Lennox, meanwhile, is preceded by a quote from the Freedom from Religion Foundation complaining about the supposed lack of science credentials of some of the authors assigned by Hedin. Lennox's book is then described dismissively as a work of "apologetics." Readers are left to assume that Lennox must be one of the alleged authors without science credentials because Lennox's background is not described in any way.

In reality, Lennox is a distinguished Professor of Mathematics at Oxford University and a Fellow in Mathematics and the Philosophy of Science at Oxford's Green Templeton College. Lennox is one of the major players in debates over science and religion, and he is certainly qualified to write a book about the relationship between science and faith. His book *God's Undertaker* has been widely praised by a number of leading scientists, theologians, and other intellectuals, including agnostic Alan Emery, Professor of Human Genetics at the University of Edinburgh, and Oxford University Professor of Human Metabolism Keith Frayn.[6]

Other hit pieces on the course were less subtle. The Huffington Post printed the following statement from a well-known atheist physicist: "Hedin promotes notions that, for the most part, have as much honest scientific support as a flat Earth."[7] What notions does this atheist have in mind? Since the course is rooted in scientific findings widely acknowledged in the mainstream astronomy/physics community, I can only guess. Sometimes people react with alarm to factual science that they haven't been accustomed to hearing. For example, a large body of scientific research shows that many aspects of the universe and planet Earth are finely tuned to allow life to exist. This can be startling to the uninitiated—which, I suspect, is why a few students (and only a very few, over many years) made comments suggesting that I had a religious bias in highlighting this body of evidence.

Fine tuning, keep in mind, is a point that scientists are broadly in agreement about. The conflict arises in working out the larger implications of this finding. Leading scientists are divided. Some see fine tuning as pointing to deism or theism, to a cosmic intelligence behind the universe. Others suggest ways to avoid this conclusion. There's a robust conversation about it among scientists at the highest levels of the profession, with even some Nobel laureates putting their money on God as the best explanation.

Notice that there is no such robust scientific controversy over whether the Earth is round or flat. The jury, as we all know, is well and truly in on that one. Accusing me of presenting evidence on par with flat-Earth advocacy is just so much ham-fisted caricature. The attack is all bluff and bluster. "Nothing to see here. Keep moving. No possible evidence for God in physics and astronomy. Carry on as you were."

In fact there is something to see here—something astonishing and very much worth slowing down to consider. If anything ever deserved a tapping of the brakes and a bit of curious rubbernecking, it's the astonishing discovery of fine tuning at both the cosmic and planetary level. We did so in my Boundaries course, and we'll do so in this book.

Establishing Atheism

So, WHAT was the immediate reaction to the attacks from Coyne and the atheist group? My department chair, who had known me for ten years, responded to the attackers. He explained that the Boundaries course was taught in the Ball State Honors College, where it is both normal and expected for courses to explore issues related to the intersection of science and society. And he confirmed that he, the dean, and the associate dean of the Honors College were all aware of the course's content. "Such a course is quite appropriate in an honors college," he concluded, "where students are expected to challenge their ideas and beliefs."

For my atheist antagonists, this wasn't good enough. The Freedom from Religion Foundation (FFRF), an atheist organization that works to remove the freedom of religion from American culture, directed a complaint against me to the president of Ball State, threatening legal action against the university unless my Boundaries class was canceled.

In their letter, the group stated that my class violated the First Amendment's religious freedom clause. In fact, the First Amendment should protect what was going on in my Boundaries course. The religion clause of the First Amendment was intended to prevent the federal government from imposing any particular religion upon its citizens. The amendment reads, "Congress shall make no law respecting an establishment of religion, or prohibiting the free exercise thereof; or abridging the freedom of speech, or of the press; or the right of the people peaceably to assemble, and to petition the Government for a redress of grievances." The amendment is important because it prevents government oppression based on belief, speech, written expression, and assembly. America was founded on freedom *of* religion, implying a tolerance of varying viewpoints of faith within the public square.

The foundational concept of academic freedom interprets these First Amendment rights within the university setting. The Ball State

University Faculty and Professional Personnel Handbook states, "Academic freedom and freedom of expression include but are not limited to the expression of ideas, philosophies, or religious beliefs, however controversial, in classroom or other academic settings."[8]

The Boundaries of Science course did not violate any aspect of the First Amendment or academic freedom. On the contrary, several Ball State students saw the attack on the course as a violation of academic freedom. In an increasingly multi-cultural society such as ours, total freedom *from* religion is untenable and suggests an antagonism towards the people and cultures we strive to understand and interact with. Among those who expressed the most distress at the Freedom from Religion Foundation's attack on my course were several international students, including those with Muslim, Buddhist, and Hindu backgrounds. Some of them protested that they had been taught that the United States was a country with freedom of religion and freedom of speech. They understood that public censorship of the course contradicted these First Amendment rights.

Many other people felt outrage at the effort to cancel the course. A national academic freedom petition that the Discovery Institute's Center for Science and Culture organized on my behalf quickly gathered over 7,000 signatures (including more than 1,200 from fellow Indiana residents), which were delivered to the president of Ball State University. The petition statement read, "We, the undersigned, urge the administration of Ball State University to support Prof. Eric Hedin's academic freedom to discuss intelligent design and related issues in the classroom. We call on you to reject demands by the Freedom from Religion Foundation to censor or punish Dr. Hedin for exercising his right to free speech."

Our university's student body president at the time, Malachi W. Randolph, sounded a similar note:

> I could say that I know many students who took Professor Hedin's classes and loved them. I could say that every student comment I've heard has been in support for Professor Hedin. I could even say that we're old enough to decide what we want to believe when controversial topics are

brought up fairly in the classroom. And while all these things are true, they don't address the issue.

The university setting has historically been fertile ground for ideas. Many major American research universities were actually religiously based. But it was their open minds and embrace (instead of fear) for outside perspectives that have allowed effective research to occur... and minds to change. (Don't make me use the "flat earth" example!)

Our university administration understands that, in order for education to be effective, there must be tolerance for ideas outside our own. That's why our Honors College offers unique classes on such topics as the Holocaust, Islam, and (ironically) Controversial Issues in Education.

Thank goodness our school isn't as narrow-minded as Dr. Jerry Coyne![9]

Alas, this may have been the highwater mark for Ball State's allegiance to academic freedom. The media attention stirred up by the ill-informed accusations from Coyne and the Freedom from Religion Foundation made it difficult to carry on with business as usual. A public university doesn't want to be perceived as going soft on science or of violating academic freedom. When the attacks came, I naïvely assumed that the university administration would quickly and vigorously stand up for me much as my department chair had, since the course had been reviewed and approved by the Honors College and was subsequently approved by a separate faculty committee as a university core curriculum course. Instead, the university issued the following response to the FFRF: "The university received a complaint from a third party late yesterday afternoon about content in a specific course offered at Ball State. We take academic rigor and academic integrity very seriously. Having just received these concerns, it is impossible to comment on them at this point. We will explore in depth the issues and concerns raised and take the appropriate actions through our established processes and procedures."

Subsequently the provost mandated that a special faculty review committee be established to determine the appropriateness of the course content, pedagogy, and academic integrity, and my credentials to teach such a course.

The *Chronicle of Higher Education* covered the story:

Andrew Seidel, a lawyer for the Freedom From Religion Foundation, an advocacy group that sent the university a letter of complaint over Mr. Hedin's teachings, said on Wednesday that his organization was "very, very pleased" with President Gora's statement.

Although Ball State has not released the results of the review of Mr. Hedin's class and it remains unclear exactly how the class will be changed, the university appeared to be taking the foundation's concerns "very seriously," Mr. Seidel said.

But John G. West, vice president of the Discovery Institute... said in an e-mail that Ms. Gora's position is "anti-academic freedom and Orwellian in the extreme."[10]

Indeed. To single out a course for such scrutiny, based on a complaint by a notoriously militant atheist group (the FFRF), raises serious questions of academic justice. Also, the four professors appointed to the review committee included two who were openly against the intelligent design movement, and one of these, along with a third member of the committee, were key speakers at a Darwin Day event at Ball State, sponsored by an atheist group. If a courtroom assembled a jury with such obvious biases, the public would be justifiably outraged.

In a June 25, 2013, article, West highlighted this problem, but also another:

According to the syllabus for Hedin's course, the vast majority of the course focuses on issues in physics, cosmology, and astronomy—not evolutionary biology," he wrote. "Yet fully half of the members of his review panel seem to have been chosen for their interest or expertise in biological evolution. At the same time, even though a central theme of Hedin's course (again, according to its syllabus) is the relationship between faith and science, not one of the reviewers appears to have expertise in the area of faith and science. Why?[11]

Having reviewed my course materials and after meeting with me for just one hour, the committee politely concluded that I practiced sound pedagogical methods and that I was qualified to teach the physics and astronomy content of the course. Beyond that, their written review contained so many misrepresentations of the course, its curriculum, and texts that, at the provost's invitation, I provided a fifteen-page response. The university, however, ignored my clarifications about the course content and how it was actually taught.

One might imagine that this was simply how the administration routinely handled such complaints. Perhaps they were inveterate conflict-avoiders and easily cowed by pressure from outside groups. It wouldn't appear so. Evolution News made the point forcefully by comparing my case to a similar one from nine years before at Ball State. The relevant excerpt is worth quoting at length:

> In both cases, there was a prominent public activist lurking behind the complaint. In 2004, the activist was conservative firebrand David Horowitz, founder of Students for Academic Freedom. In 2013, the activist is atheist Darwinian biologist Jerry Coyne....
>
> The contrast with how BSU handled the complaint against Professor Wolfe couldn't be more stark. Instead of appointing a review panel or launching an extensive investigation in 2004, BSU officials quickly circled the wagons around Professor Wolfe and defended him to the media, the state legislature, and the public at large. The minimal investigation of the complaint against Wolfe seems to have consisted of the provost talking to both Wolfe's supervisor and Professor Wolfe and reading some letters. The provost apparently did not even bother to interview the student who had come forward to allege discriminatory treatment in class. As a result, the Wolfe complaint was quickly disposed of....
>
> Compare that approach to the Hedin case today. By any objective measure, the complaint submitted by the Freedom from Religion Foundation against Hedin was far less serious, and far less credible, than the allegations lodged against Professor Wolfe. In saying this, I am not taking sides about who was right in the Wolfe controversy. Professor Wolfe vig-

orously challenged the allegations made against him at the time, and David Horowitz has continued to defend his criticisms of Wolfe. My point is merely that the complaint originally leveled against Wolfe put forward much more serious allegations of misconduct than the complaint against Hedin. The complaint against Wolfe identified a student by name who made specific charges of discriminatory treatment and the intimidation of students. By contrast, the complaint against Hedin did not identify any student who was willing to complain on the record against Hedin.

Instead, it merely highlighted a few anonymous (and ambiguous) comments from RateMyProfessor.com, a website that doesn't even verify whether those posting comments are in fact college students, let alone whether they ever took courses from the professor in question.

More importantly, and unlike in the Wolfe case, the complaint against Hedin did not allege that Hedin had actually intimidated students or threatened to grade them down for holding different beliefs than himself.

Despite the fact that the allegations against Hedin were far less weighty than those against Wolfe, BSU's current provost Terry King did not dispose of FFRF's complaint quickly. Instead, he created a review panel that appears to be stacked with faculty with conflicts of interest who are likely to be hostile to Professor Hedin's point of view. In the meantime, Professor Hedin has been left hanging without any clear support from the top officials at his university. It is now more than forty days (and counting) since FFRF's complaint—a far cry from the ten days it took for the university to resolve the more serious complaint against Professor Wolfe.[12]

Discovery Institute also advocated on my behalf to state legislators, who sent a letter to BSU president Jo Ann Gora and the Ball State board of trustees in March of 2014 expressing concern about the policy she had instituted "restricting faculty speech on intelligent design." The three senators and one representative wrote, "We are concerned about whether improper procedures were followed while investigating Professor Eric Hedin's course, and whether an ad hoc committee appointed to investigate him was filled with persons with conflicts of interest, who were predisposed to be hostile to his viewpoint…. We are also concerned about the cancellation of Hedin's class and the policy you announced last summer restricting faculty speech on intelligent design."[13]

The letter resulted in top legislators meeting with university officials about my situation later that semester.

Some may complain that allowing students to learn about scientific evidence that might conflict with the paradigm of naturalism could incline them to believe in a divine creator. So, does teaching that scientific evidence equate with teaching religion in a science course? Is censorship the preferred option? Atheism has never been and is not now the established religion of our country. The First Amendment, after all, forbids the establishment of any religion, and it certainly wasn't intended to privilege the atheistic worldview over non-atheistic religious outlooks, as much as some atheists might wish that to be the case. Nor do scientific discussions of the potential limits of naturalism constitute an unfair treatment of atheism, for if atheism were true, an objective pursuit of the evidence from nature would support it. Only if atheism has something to hide can the objective pursuit of evidence threaten to undermine it.

Student Comments on The Boundaries of Science

SEVERAL FORMER students wrote letters to the editors of local newspapers or to the university administration in support of their experience in my class. At the time Discovery Institute's Joshua Youngkin reported, "Although the committee is apparently not required to examine witnesses to or take statements on the conduct of Dr. Hedin's course, some of Dr. Hedin's students have privately and voluntarily offered such statements to BSU's president, Jo Ann Gora. This we discovered through public documents requests to BSU."

One student wrote:

Students were encouraged to share any and all thoughts we had, especially if it was a different perspective than one already shared. Discussions included a wide variety of topics, such as the nature of time and reality, the definition of truth, whether there were categories of life, and the fine-tuning of universal parameters for life to exist. These conversations were fascinating, engaging, and challenging in the best of ways. Never once did I personally hear any complaints from my fellow students; on the contrary, the mood was always positive—we enjoyed stretching our minds. Dr. Hedin was always respectful and kind.[14]

This student also voiced concern about some of the sensationalistic mischaracterizations in the media of me and of the course. "Simply on the words of people who did not actually attend Hedin's class (and can therefore not make a reliable assessment of his methods), Hedin's credibility will be trashed and he will continue to be portrayed as a professor who did nothing but decry evolutionary theory and criticize non-Christians (neither of which, of course, are true)," she wrote. "This is already happening—someone in the IndyStar.com article compared him to a Holocaust denier."[15]

This student was one of many people who rallied to my cause. After the initial spate of hate emails from atheists sputtered out, I was greatly encouraged by a steady flow of supportive letters and emails from former students, friends, and people I'd never met. One former student wrote, "I just read in the news the controversy over your class. I just wanted to encourage you in the good that you have done thus far on campus. Your class has been my favorite class in my college career." She added that it really helped her understand what science was about, and to think freely.

The last section I taught of the Boundaries of Science course was in the middle of the accusations and media attention. One of my students in that section described the course's discussion-based format:

The only time the professor even delves into the students' debates is to refute any arguments that are just blatantly incorrect, do not consider all of the possibilities, or seem derogatory and opinionated in nature, *much like the arguments posed by the people who are generating this tirade* against Professor Hedin. I'm an agnostic and I find absolutely nothing wrong with his teachings… as far as intelligent and thought-provoking discussions go, it is one of the most *innovative* classes I have had during my time at Ball State.[16] [emphasis in original]

Not once did anyone from the university ever contact me to try to contradict the truth of what I taught. The university administration simply said that I couldn't continue teaching the course. But what they said I couldn't teach (religion) was not what I taught. In ignoring the many comments and letters from students writing in support of the course, and in and heeding only the anti-theists who wanted to label my course religious propaganda, the administration built up a straw man which could then be torn down. This accomplished their purpose; the course was canceled, with the administration manufacturing an impropriety to serve as the basis of the censure: violation of "academic integrity."

As West commented later, "In the Orwellian world of Ball State's president, academic freedom apparently means only the 'freedom' to support the majority's view. This is exactly how the academic 'consensus' against the theory of intelligent design is maintained—by intimidation, fiat, and legal threats."[17]

To make the administration's position even more untenable and dubious than it already was, they soon defended another honors course in which the sole assigned textbook was an anthology of anti-religious essays titled *What Is Your Dangerous Idea?* The BSU administration's public relations arm claimed that some of the essays in the anthology were pro-religion. But this was not the case; only a small handful of the essay titles even appeared to support traditional religion, and in fact the essays themselves were militantly anti-religious.

The problem isn't that such a textbook was assigned at a public university. The problem is the flagrant inconsistency of the administration. Science writer Casey Luskin explained in a March 17, 2014, essay:

> BSU spokesman Tony Proudfoot tries to defend the course on the grounds that the book includes religion-friendly chapters, and therefore isn't a polemic against religion. In fact, BSU has badly misrepresented the hard-to-miss anti-religious goals of the book, as well as the three supposedly religion-friendly chapters it cites.... of the three chapters BSU cites as being religion-friendly, one has nothing to do with religion and the other two are explicitly anti-religious.

... *What Is Your Dangerous Idea?* is framed, billed, and marketed as a book of ideas by leading new atheist-types. The intended readership seems to be intellectual atheists, as its cover advertises the fact that the introduction is by new atheist (and evolutionary psychologist) Steven Pinker, and the afterword is by leading new atheist Richard Dawkins.

Indeed, the man behind *What Is Your Dangerous Idea?*, who served as its editor, is John Brockman, has been called one of "the 25 most influential living atheists." ...

Again, this book is the sole textbook for BSU's "Dangerous Ideas" course according to the syllabus supplied to us by BSU through a public documents request. If it had been assigned along with readings from a different perspective, that would have been a different situation. Indeed, if BSU allowed other professors (like Eric Hedin) to present an alternative view about the compatibility of faith and science in their classes, then BSU could claim that this book is simply part of allowing a forum for various views, and that would be fine. But BSU canceled Professor Hedin's course—and now it is defending a course that uses as its lone textbook an anti-religious polemic.

The authors in *What Is Your Dangerous Idea?* have every right to express their views, and likewise, individual faculty at public universities may, generally speaking, critique religion. But when a state university permits religion-bashing in the name of science while censoring other views, that government institution has strayed into constitutionally treacherous waters.[18]

If my Boundaries course had, for instance, presented only the statements and arguments of famous physicists and astronomers promoting the idea that fine tuning is evidence of a supreme designer, this would have been roughly the mirror opposite of the Dangerous Ideas course, and one might reasonably have expected the administration to either support both courses, or to disapprove of both courses. But in fact my course pointed students to scientists and arguments on both sides of the fine-tuning debate, whereas the Dangerous Ideas course had at its center a textbook that was unswervingly pro-atheist. And yet it was my course that was canceled and the all-in-for-atheism course that was studiously defended.

Here, no doubt, some atheists will accuse me of "whining" about the administration's decision. This is a common attack strategy against anyone speaking up about injustice. Call it whining. Call it speaking truth to power. Call it whatever you want, but ask yourself, why are the atheists so keen to only have their side of the story told? What evidence are they afraid of you hearing?

My Boundaries course had been taken away under pressure from atheists keen to shut down the sort of open-ended conversations I encouraged in the course, conversations that surfaced scientific evidence which does not easily fit into an atheistic paradigm. I mourned the loss of that course and moved on. But the drama for me wasn't quite over. You see, I was a tenure-track professor, but I wasn't yet tenured. Another battle lay on the horizon, one for my job at Ball State. How that one ended I'll save for a later chapter. Now I want to begin the work of giving fresh life to some of the material from my canceled Boundaries course, through the pages of this book.

I say "some of the material" because a single book of this length cannot cover all the material included in my honors university course. To get the breadth of direct exposure that my Boundaries course provided, you'd have to read the material by the atheistic/naturalistic scientists that I assigned there, material that in these pages I only cite, summarize and, at times, briefly quote. I will strive to present their arguments accurately, to be sure, but the primary aim of this book is to present the evidence and arguments that the atheists who targeted me don't want you to see.

Questions from the Edge

I ENCOURAGED the students in my Boundaries of Science course to ask some big questions. The course was canceled after some of the questions, evidence, and arguments covered in the course were deemed radioactive by the Ball State administration. This book won't shy away from those big questions. We'll ask those questions and, in looking for answers, we'll consider clues from the body of accepted scientific evidence.

The great ancient Greek philosopher Socrates said the unexamined life isn't worth living. In our frenetic, plugged-in society, living an unexamined life is as easy as breathing. When do we have the opportunity to stop and explore questions of significance to our lives? So often our conversations are limited to the breezy small talk of the moment, or to practicalities of the hour. But our lives mean more than checking off a to-do list, paying the bills, and feeding our various appetites.

If you've chosen to read this book, you've determined to pause at the intersection of science and some deep questions about our existence, refusing to be swept along by the push and crush of the urgent. But, you may wonder, can science speak to questions of deep significance? Your notion of science may call to mind things like pressure gauges, lab mice, black holes, complex math, and such, all of which can seem far removed from questions of meaning and purpose. We'll see, however, that some scientific discoveries do cast significant light on questions many of us have about the meaning of life.

Religion, the arts, philosophy, and other fields of human inquiry and experience also can contribute to answering deep questions related to our existence, and sometimes much more directly. So, why use science as an avenue into such matters?

Because science is the study of our natural world, and we all have that world in common. We all live in the same universe, and the laws of nature affect us all the same—whether we believe in them or not, and whether we are aware of them or not. The common ground of nature is a starting point that includes everyone.

What is the Meaning of Your Existence, or the Purpose of Life?

When I've surveyed students about their views on the meaning and purpose of life, their answers reveal a wide range of perspectives:

- To live for others.

- To live life to the fullest.
- To learn.
- To live for God.
- To live and then die.
- To procreate.
- To be part of the food chain.
- There is no meaning.
- I've never thought about the meaning of life.

Out of all these typical responses from my students during my time at Ball State, the most common one was usually the fourth one listed here: "To live for God." But not uncommon were "To live and then die," "to procreate," and "to be part of the food chain." Some students giving the latter answers explained that they answered in that way because of what they had learned concerning the theory of evolution. But what if every human has off-the-scale significance? How sad would it be to fail to grasp one's own great significance.

As unfortunate as that seems to me, the response which most impressed upon me the importance of asking such a question was the last one on the list: "I've never thought about the meaning of life." To drift through life without direction, thoughtless about whether a purpose for living even exists, strikes me as such a waste of the human capacity for reflection and wonder.

So, how about you? What would you say is the purpose of life? And what can science tell us about this big question? Are there clues in the science of origins? In the chapters ahead, we'll look carefully at some of the fascinating backstory of life on planet Earth. We'll discover that this universe exhibits fine tuning for supporting life, and that our planet is remarkable in its life-supporting properties.

We'll learn how the very atomic elements that make up our bodies, the ground under our feet, and the air we breathe had their genesis in the nuclear furnaces of massive stars. We'll consider explanations for why the universe is the way it is, and weigh those explanations against the scientific evidence.

Of course, in the end, you are free to believe whatever you choose, and we'll even consider the implications of the fact that you are free to believe whatever you choose. But for now, let's move on to a second big question I regularly posed in my Boundaries of Science course.

What One Question Would You Most Like Answered?

THE REASON for this question is that the questions we would most like answered can reveal what's most important to us. Would your question be one of these?

- How do we know what to believe?
- What happens when you die? Is there life after death?
- Is heaven real, and how can I get there?
- Is there a God?
- How should I live my life?
- How did the universe begin?
- How did life begin?
- Is there life on other planets?
- What's the purpose of life?

Those are some of the common responses my students gave at Ball State. The most common ones had to do with questions about the existence of God and our relationship with him. Other common questions centered around science topics relating to origins. And the question of purpose, or just, "Why?" was often on the list. A range of scientific disciplines can speak to several of these questions—physics, astronomy, cosmology (the study of the universe as a whole), biology and biophysics, and the science of consciousness, to name just a few. Will the evidence we explore answer every question definitively? No, but it can provide some potentially useful clues.

Climbing the Mountain of Science

A THIRD big question deals with science itself: Can science yield material explanations for everything? Some of my students answered yes, and their reasoning was pretty straightforward: science explains more and more as time goes on, and will eventually explain everything. *No* *Gödels*

This response indicates a faith that although science can't explain everything yet, it will in the future. What assumptions lie behind this *incompleteness* *Theorem* view? One is that the cosmos is a closed natural system, self contained. If that's true, then natural laws govern everything in the cosmos, including every detail of our lives. This assumption deserves a thorough examination.

To be sure, it's easy to see how one might assume that purely material explanations will know no bounds. In the past, what is sometimes referred to as the "god-of-the-gaps" approach filled holes in our knowledge of the world with supernatural miracles. If you didn't understand what causes storms, or why a plague visits your village every few years, you might just shrug and attribute it to the gods. A handy explanation, but invoking a miracle every time you encounter something in nature you don't understand is a poor way to advance our knowledge of the natural world. The founders of modern science recognized this and discouraged god-of-the-gaps thinking.

Various natural phenomena attributed to divine intervention have given way to natural explanations over the years as scientific knowledge advanced. Some people have thereby assumed that this process will go right on until everything in the cosmos has a fully satisfactory, material explanation. But is this extrapolation warranted? Consider an illustration. I grew up hiking the alpine trails and peaks of the Cascade Mountains. After I toiled up the thickly forested mountainside, the trees would thin out and the view would open up across the valley below. Alpine firs and spruces, looking like perfect Christmas trees, poked up through a tidy undergrowth of green and purple heather dotted with late-blooming wildflowers. But while these views were certainly charming, they were not the ultimate goal of those hikes. When the trail was long and our packs heavy, we often longed to reach our destination, and it was easy to fall prey to "false summits." On the way up, certain high points on the trail can look like the summit to those who haven't taken the trail before, but those points turn out to be just a shoulder or a knoll, with the trail continuing on higher.

Seeking to understand the universe is akin to such hikes, with each step on the way representing a further understanding of the laws of nature. The false summits are places where people wrongly concluded that science could take us no further, and then it was discovered that science could indeed explain the given mystery in purely natural terms. But naturalists would have us believe that because we have encountered several such false summits, there is no true summit, that it's all just shoulders and knolls—false summits—unending, and that every apparent limit to purely material explanations is always only apparent. But that doesn't follow. It's still logically possible that there indeed are things that cannot be explained by purely natural causes.

To expand our illustration, if we picture the scientific enterprise as not a mountain trek but the exploration of a vast mountain range stretching beyond the horizon, we can expect to continue to discover fresh vistas and many new things, but also many real summits along with some false ones.

Simply making up a rule that says we won't ever regard anything as a real summit—that is, a real limit to what the blind forces of nature can accomplish—doesn't magically grant to natural forces powers they may simply not possess.

In the pages that follow we will explore evidence from nature that suggests there indeed are limits to what nature without intelligent guidance can accomplish. In this we will be following ordinary canons of reasoning about clues and causes. If, for example, you find that your car has a flat tire, you don't expect that the problem will remedy itself if you just wait a few days (or a few millennia). If a neighbor's pet goldfish dies in its fishbowl, we don't try waiting a couple of weeks to see if it will return to life. Our study of nature will reveal evidence suggesting that neither should we expect an interstellar gas cloud to eventually turn itself into a goldfish.

Evidence that nature is limited and unable to generate some of the things we observe around us also suggests that reality may be bigger than naturalism. It suggests that consciousness, significance, meaning, and purpose may not be mere foam on a churning universe of particles but in fact aspects of a deeper, immaterial reality.

Philosopher Antony Flew, once described as "the world's most notorious atheist," committed himself to following the evidence wherever it leads. In the course of that investigation, he concluded that over the last hundred years, scientists "have built a philosophically compelling vision of a rational universe that sprang from a divine Mind" and "as it happens, this is the particular view of the world that I now find to be the soundest philosophical explanation of a multitude of phenomena encountered by scientists and laypeople alike."[19] Specifically, he cited three questions that ultimately led him to renounce atheism:

1. How did the laws of nature come to be?
2. How did life originate from non-life?
3. How did the universe come into existence?[20]

We will explore those questions and more in these pages.

Is the evidence that led Flew out of atheism overruled by other reasonable considerations? This book, an outgrowth of my Boundaries of Science course, provides an uncensored opportunity for readers to engage this body of evidence and ask the questions many of us would like to thoughtfully explore—questions about the meaning of our existence and whether the world is ultimately just so many particles in the cosmic void.

In my Boundaries course I strove to stay above the fray and focused on asking thought-provoking questions while introducing physical evidence relevant to the discussion, including scientific evidence that may not have been considered in a course biased towards naturalism. Here in these pages I also strive to be as fair as possible with the evidence, but I will go a step further than I did in my Boundaries course by laying out the particular chain of reasoning that for me strongly affirms that nature is the work of a masterful intelligence. I intend to make a case, based on physical evidence and widely accepted canons of reasoning, that we were purposefully made, and made for a purpose.

2. Rooted in Reality

One of the first Boundaries of Science classes I taught met in a two-story circular building just across the road from the campus duck pond. Among the students in this class were two young men who turned out to be outspoken atheists. They frequently dominated class discussions by vociferously arguing their viewpoints, especially on anything having to do with evolution. It got to the point that other students complained to me about their behavior, and I had to ask the two to tone it down and give others a fair chance to offer their opinions.

In spite of this, when class was over each day, I often ended up walking with these two for about ten minutes across campus on our way to our next classes. We always continued the class discussion topics as we went, and I ended up having more of a relationship with these two students than with any of the others in the class. My guess is that it was because they sensed that I truly wanted to foster open exploration of the ideas raised in the class, and because the three of us were mutually interested in some big, ultimate questions swirling around origins science. And since I rooted the discussions in scientific knowledge, our conversations inside and outside the classroom were based on common ground.

Grounding discussions in scientific knowledge is quite different from allowing those conversations to be ruled over by the "science says" trump card. We can sometimes take science for granted, as a sort of knowledge-generating machine, without really understanding how it actually works. Because of this, we would do well to ask some fundamental questions about the nature of the scientific enterprise itself.

How Do We Know What We Know?

Science is about knowing, but how do we know what we know? The most obvious way we learn is through our senses, by seeing, hearing, and touching. Can we trust our senses? In courts of law, we rely upon eye-witness accounts as valuable evidence. Often, even honest eyewitnesses disagree, since each one may focus on a different aspect of the event in question, and each person witnesses it from a different perspective. All the same, the justice system depends on our being able to sort through various eyewitness accounts to get closer to the truth and, in many cases, reach conclusions "beyond a reasonable doubt," to use the language of the courts. This method of reaching conclusions about things not wit-nessed directly by judge and jury isn't unique to court cases, of course. We learn many things by being informed by others, either face to face or by reading what others have written.

How reliable is second-hand information? Clearly, it's only as reli-able as the source. For example, how do we know that the city of Vienna exists? If we haven't had the opportunity of traveling there ourselves, we would probably believe it exists based on reports of people we trust. How do we know that matter is composed of atoms, which in turn are made of electrons, protons, and neutrons? If you remember that fact from a science class, you "know" this by believing those who have done experi-ments that reveal such a picture of matter. Very few people, however, even among scientists, will ever see for themselves the first-hand evi-dence for this knowledge.

My point is that the way we come to know many things is a more complicated process than it may seem at first blush. Just getting my students to recognize this is an important first step in thinking clearly about scientific evidence and scientific knowledge.

What is Assumed in Doing Science?

SCIENCE IS driven by the assumption that we can understand nature and grow in knowledge. If that assumption weren't true, the efforts of science would be in vain. Science also assumes that a reality exists "out there," which can be accessed by anyone with the ability to make observations. Science also holds that the laws of nature are essentially constant. This

Lorenervice invariance?

assumption animates scientists' attempts to repeat experiments in order to try to verify previous results.

In the late 1980s I was working in Stockholm on a plasma physics experiment called Extrap. This high-tech device in the basement of the Alfvén Laboratory employed powerful magnetic fields to temporarily confine hot plasma (ionized hydrogen gas). The goal was to study how magnetically confined plasmas might one day produce fusion energy. (The lab was named after Hannes Alfvén, who won the 1970 Nobel Prize in Physics for his research on plasmas, and who still had his office on the second floor of the building.) While working there, big news came from the States about researchers who had supposedly succeeded in generating fusion energy from a cold fuel source. This report sparked a lot of excitement, since cold fusion held the promise of a new, nearly unlimited energy source. But attempts by other scientists to repeat the initial results failed, so the excitement faded and the scientific community subsequently rejected the claim.

The story highlights the importance of repeatability in experiments. Science assumes that the "reality" of the physical world is governed by laws and principles which are rational, universal, and stable over time, meaning that a carefully designed and executed experiment should be able to be repeated.

These assumptions have a solid basis. While scientific study of the universe has only occurred for a fraction of the age of the universe, scientific observations allow us to see clear back to the infancy of the universe. Take the study of distant stars. Some are only a few light years away. The light from a star twenty light years away shows us what was happening with that star twenty years ago, since it takes twenty years for light to travel twenty light years. But we also observe celestial objects that are thousands and even many millions of light years away. In such cases it's like we're watching archival movie footage of the celestial object from thousands or millions of years ago. (More on this in Chapter 5.)

Studying many different parts of the universe and at widely different time periods in this way confirms the universality and constancy of the laws of nature. The relationship between stellar brightness and a star's surface temperature, for example, is the same for distant stars (seen as they were in the distant past) as it is for closer stars (seen as they were more recently). Many of the constants of nature conspire together to determine the energy output of stars and their specific spectral wavelengths. Among others, these constants include the speed of light, the gravitational constant, Planck's constant, the charge on electrons and protons, and the masses of the fundamental particles. So, when astronomers observe stars, whether near or far, and see the same results, they affirm that the way the universe works remains constant throughout time.

What is Reality?

IF SCIENCE assumes a reality that's accessible for study, this invites a still more basic question: "What is reality?" Some thoughts and questions from my students on the nature of reality include:

- Reality is what we see, hear, touch, taste, and smell.
- Reality is whatever we make it.
- Reality can be determined scientifically.
- Are feelings part of reality?
- Is there a reality "out there," or is it just in our heads?

Let's stay with that last one for a minute. Can we be sure reality is "out there," existing separate from us and our perceptions? Scientific confidence in an aspect of reality is increased if different observers all measure the same value for a physical constant—say, the acceleration of gravity at the surface of the Earth. From this we can reasonably conclude that the force of gravity is "out there," is real, and not a figment of any one person's imagination.

Another force of nature is the electromagnetic force. If this immaterial force didn't really exist, if it weren't the same for all who measured it, our electronic technology would not work. Being able to discover the stable electrical properties of semiconductors and other materials has enabled scientists worldwide to design and build microelectronic circuits. As a result, computers, smart phones, and digital cameras have become commonplace and affordable.

I mentioned above that a goal of science is to obtain an increasingly accurate handle on reality. One reason for this is that we value truth for its own sake. But another reason for this goal is that the more we understand physical reality, the more successful we'll be when interacting with it. For example, advancements in technology and medicine are the results of an accurate understanding of physics and biology. Conversely, an inaccurate view of the physical world eventually leads to failure in our dealings with it. A person who still believed in the geocentric model of the solar system would not succeed in plotting the trajectory of a space probe to the planet Saturn. More drastically, those who thought gravity only applied to other objects and not to themselves wouldn't live long if their mistaken belief led them to step off a cliff.

So, to summarize: Science has revealed a definiteness and a specificity to nature. We can say that nature has certain properties and not others. The entire physical universe reveals a particular objective reality. What we believe about physical reality makes a difference in how effective our interactions with nature will be—in other words, what we believe about the physical realm *matters*.

What about the spiritual realm? Does what we believe about God also matter? It seems reasonable that the saying, "It doesn't matter what you believe as long as you're sincere," could be no more valid about the spiritual realm than the physical. So if God and the spiritual realm don't exist—if they are just fictions—then rightly understanding this should matter in important ways to us. And if God and the spiritual realm do exist—if they are real—then having a fundamentally accurate belief about this reality should also matter. For one, it would provide us with important resources in addressing questions of deep human significance, such as whether free will is possible.

You may have heard it said that only science can provide reliable answers to significant questions about reality. But "science alone can provide reliable answers" is not a statement *of* science; it's a statement *about* science.[1] Holding this position is to step out of science into the realm of philosophy. Moreover, the statement is self-discrediting. If science alone can provide reliable answers, then the extra-scientific philosophical claim that "science alone can provide reliable answers" isn't itself reliable. It isn't science, after all.

Finding Reality

HUMANS ARE always wondering such things as, "What's over the top of the hill?" The astronomer extends this impulse into space: What's it like under the cloud layer of that moon orbiting Saturn? What's it like at the center of our galaxy? What's a faraway quasar really like? The universe of far-flung galaxies seems to go on and on, beyond imagining, but our hearts long for more than just endless space and matter. Does that longing point to something real beyond the physical cosmos?

To answer that question in the negative isn't a more scientific answer than its opposite. The question is philosophical—metaphysical—and so too are the answers. Conflating science with a philosophical viewpoint—materialism—is neither properly scientific nor rational. The scientific materialist would say that we must only consider purely material explanations if we are to behave as proper scientists. But again, that's a dogmatic philosophical rule, not a scientific observation. We won't get closer to knowing the truth by genuflecting before a dogmatic rule. We would do well, rather, to tease out the evidence and follow it where it leads.

The materialist regards as a mirage all that distinguishes humans from inanimate matter: free will, reason, sacrificial love, grace, the sense that every person is significant and precious. The materialist must even regard the human mind and consciousness, the most immediate thing each of us experiences, as mere froth on some physio-chemical brain process. But what if the cosmos really is telling us of something grander than particles in the void? What if the heavens really do declare the glory of someone greater than the heavens, greater than stars and stardust?

We long to be known, and if the ancient catechism has it right, we long to worship. A finely tuned universe that points to a cosmic fine tuner—a designing mind of mind-boggling power and artistry—sheds light on that longing and points the way to how we can fulfill it. An endless proliferation of unobservable universes—invoked to explain away a fine-tuner—could never satisfy our sense of eternity.

Why Is There Something Rather Than Nothing?

HERE WE come to a bedrock question: Why is there an *is*? Why is there anything? Students in my honors course often responded to this question with these sorts of comments.

- Something has always existed.
- "Nothing" can't produce something.
- Nothing is only a negation of something, and is not itself anything.

We had a small-group discussion on this question in one of my honors classes, where we happened to be sitting outside on an early summer day. After the discussion, a student in the group gestured to our natural surroundings and said that something beyond nature must have been responsible for bringing the natural world into being. This student had earlier described himself as an atheist, but our discussion led him to express a different view.

Can pondering a question this basic—why something rather than nothing?—really have such a profound impact on what we believe? At the very least it opens up a can of philosophical worms that many people never consider. What is nothing? Is it the emptiness between galaxies? No. Science tells us that even empty space is not nothing, that space itself is something, a fabric of sorts that can be bent by gravity, stretched, and even has energy.

Absolute nothing cannot produce something, because if it had that ability, it would have something, and so it wouldn't be nothing. From this we can conclude that something has always existed because something exists now. So far, we're just using logic.

We also know from science that the physical stuff of our universe came into existence in the finite past. So, something brought our universe into existence, and that something could not have been part of our universe; otherwise our universe would already have existed, and what already exists cannot then be brought into existence. (Again, we're just using logic here.) We can therefore call the cause of our universe a transcendent cause, since it transcends our universe.

Multiverse, Same as the First

SOME SCIENTISTS have postulated that our universe, as big as it is, is actually only one of a very large number of other universes. This combined set of universes is referred to as the *multiverse*. The hypothesized additional universes are impossible to detect from our universe. Everything we can observe and detect is limited to our universe. Despite this, the multiverse hypothesis has been used as part of a theoretical construct to say that our universe could have originated naturally. Our universe is said to have formed within the multiverse by means of an overarching universe generator. (Keep in mind that none of these ideas are confirmed by observational evidence.) The idea of a multiverse also is invoked to try to explain in materialistic terms the curious fact that the laws and constants of our universe are fine tuned to allow for life. On this view, our universe is just one of the lucky universes with a set of laws and constants that allows for life. We will take up the fine-tuning issue a bit later. Here let's stay focused on the multiverse hypothesis as an explanation for the origin of our universe.

For the sake of argument, could the multiverse hypothesis explain the origin of our universe in terms of natural, physical processes? In some respects, we are running into semantic difficulties here. One might define the "universe" as the entire extent of everything physical that exists. Some might add to that a qualifier—everything physical that exists and is causally connected to the visible universe, however remotely. But notice that even with this qualifier, the multiverse—or at least the universe-generating system—is already included in the definition of the universe, since the universe generator is both physical and is linked to our visible universe in a causal chain. So, in an important sense, the pro-

2. Rooted in Reality / 45

posed multiverse is the universe, with our "universe" simply being part of this larger multi-part universe.

Or if one wishes to maintain a firm line between our universe and the multiverse, one still has the question of the origin of the multiverse's universe-generating system. None of these physical entities is a good candidate for an eternally existent entity, so whether a multiverse genie is invoked or no, an origins mystery remains.

If an eternally existing physical universe or multiverse is unsupported by evidence, and if something cannot come from nothing, then what explanation is left? Could something that transcends matter and energy provide a sufficient explanation for the origin of our fine-tuned universe? An immaterial cause? A mind? Is such an idea consistent with the discoveries of modern science? Let's delve deeper into the evidence and see.

What Is the Most Incomprehensible Thing about the Universe?

ALBERT EINSTEIN said the most incomprehensible thing about the universe was that it was comprehensible. To be sure, Einstein had a better grasp of how the physical universe works than most of us do. But is it not remarkable that one of the most brilliant scientific minds in history found it perplexing that we could comprehend the universe? Yes, some of us might say, "It's not very comprehensible to me—I barely passed physics!" We all have our specialties. But, returning to the question, why should *any* human be able to understand so much of the deep nature of physical reality?

Certainly, just to live we learn something about nature—the rhythms of day and night and the passing of the seasons, the ability of fire to cook food, and so on. But why should any human minds be able to track with the mathematics of electrodynamics, the counter-intuitive results of relativity theory, or the subtleties of quantum mechanics? Human minds have now mastered all of these sufficiently to enable us to build practical technologies based upon our understanding of them.

What prepared someone like Einstein to come up with a groundbreaking theory of space and time? Einstein's theory of general relativity made precise predictions about an unheard-of phenomenon, namely the bending of starlight as it passed by the sun on the way to Earth. Within a few years of the theory's publication in 1916, scientists confirmed Einstein's predictions from observations gathered during a perfect solar eclipse.

The comprehensibility of the universe is an underlying assumption of science. The validity of this assumption is verified by the overall success of the scientific endeavor. But why is the universe such that it obeys deep mathematical regularities, ones we can tame for our use? And why is it that humanity has the capacity to comprehend these deep patterns?

Consider that second question first. The naturalistic view of human origins assumes that random interactions between atoms and forces produced you, me, Einstein, and everyone else. Evolutionary theory is based upon survival of the fittest (defined as the ones that both survive and produce the most offspring). Would such a mechanism for the origin of our species be likely to develop mathematical, scientific, and artistic geniuses?

What gave Michelangelo the ability to chisel away marble until a supple form of beauty and evocative emotion emerged from the stone, as in Michelangelo's David? How could a musical genius like Mozart even exist?[2] The naturalistic theory for the origin of humans maintains that who we are stems from the repetitive selection of procreative advantage, not mathematical or artistic prowess. The Darwinian mechanism is single-focused, and developing enhanced ability for abstract mathematics or artistic expression is off target.

The naturalistic model admits no directing intelligence. It's only matter interacting by mechanistic pushes or pulls. But could any of these effects by themselves produce humans with all their varied talents, or even a single cell of such a creature?[3] There would seem to be a fundamental disconnect between the soulless, unguided mechanisms available to Darwinian materialism and humans endowed with both soul and mind.

What if we consider the question from a theistic perspective? Having a mind to comprehend nuclei and neutron stars, and the ability to create works of artistic genius, may be a considerably less surprising outcome if humans are made in the image of a being who is himself an artistic and mathematical genius. We will explore the scientific evidence for this in more depth in later chapters.

What's Stronger, Truth or a Lie?

WHICH HAS more power, the truth or a lie? I have found that this is a good question for getting students to ponder the nature of truth and falsehood, and to think about what effects scientific truths, and false scientific claims, might have on us. Student responses to this question include the following:

- Lies can be very convincing.
- Lies have no essence in themselves—they are only a distortion of the truth.
- Lies need to be propped up; truth just is.
- Truth corresponds to reality, and so it is permanent.

If a reality exists (and our common experience strongly suggests that it does), then truth can exist. Truth means an accurate description of reality. A goal of science, as mentioned earlier, is to come closer to an accurate understanding of reality. In this sense, the goal of science is to discover truth. A scientific theory or conclusion may be in error, but the reality of the universe allows us to cross-check our results. Further study and observations will likely refine the theory and bring it more in line with truth.

The process of the scientific method has a good track record of clearing up misconceptions and false ideas about nature as more evidence comes to light. However, this correction process can get bogged down when the scientific method is hijacked by political or religious agendas. Such agendas seek to override the evidence of nature by imposing presuppositions that block the truth. For example, when the Big Bang model of the origin of the universe was first proposed, some scientists sought to dismiss it. They did so not because the evidence for it was weak, but because the theory implied a beginning out of nothing, which disagreed with their presupposition of naturalism. If their dogmatic insistence had won over the community of cosmologists, progress toward the truth might have stalled.

How long can such false assumptions stand? Hopefully only temporarily, since lies have no essence in themselves; the truth of reality will eventually shine through, provided there remains a contingent of competent, truth-seeking scientists undeterred by groupthink and dogma.

What Has Science Revealed about the Universe?

Science has shown us some features of the universe that deserve careful consideration, discoveries that may shed light on the question of whether there is something more to reality than our physical universe. Here are some of the main "reveals" that we discussed in the Boundaries of Science course:

- The universe had an origin in the finite past—not just its matter and energy, but also our universe's space-time continuum.
- The fundamental parameters of the universe are fine tuned to allow for life.
- The specific conditions on planet Earth are fine tuned to support a fantastic variety of living things.

What should we make of such discoveries? Many scientists, philosophers, and theologians have grappled with these matters and arrived at a variety of opinions. Some claim nothing but chance as the ultimate reason for our existence. Some implicitly deify nature, saying it destined us to exist. Others see strong evidence of intelligent design.

It isn't always a good idea to "simply trust the experts." The experts, after all, have been known to be glaringly wrong, either due to honest mistakes or because the experts in a particular case had this or that motive drawing them away from an objective, honest consideration of the evidence. But notice in this case that there isn't even an option to "simply trust the experts." That's because the experts disagree.

There's nothing for it, then, but to weigh the evidence yourself and try to reach your own conclusions, particularly where the key evidence on a question can be made user-friendly to non-specialists. That's what I aim to do in the pages ahead. Accessible discussions of each of the main points in our list above are presented in the chapters that follow.

In Chapter 3 we will look at some of the basic laws and principles of nature, discovered through scientific experiments and observations. Some of these "laws of nature" will seem like common sense, matching well with our everyday experiences. Other aspects of nature may strike you as hard to believe, completely counterintuitive. But that's where it really gets interesting! As has been observed, "The universe is not only queerer than we suppose, but queerer than we can suppose."[4]

Strange, and yet strangely comprehensible. Buckle up. The ride's just begun.

3. THE COSMIC QUEST

IN RECENT YEARS, A SCIENCE EDUCATION INITIATIVE HAS INCLUDED a specific reference to naturalism as a supposed hallmark of science. The full list was billed as "Hallmarks of Science" and included the three premises below:

1. "Modern science seeks explanations for observed phenomena that rely solely on natural causes."
2. "Science progresses through the creation and testing of models of nature that explain the observations as simply as possible."
3. "A scientific model must make testable predictions about natural phenomena that will force us to revise or abandon the model if the predictions do not agree with observations."[1]

Most of this is fine, but it's worth asking, is the first premise subject to the third premise? What if our study of some natural phenomenon showed that it could not arise solely from natural causes? In such a case, we would have to abandon either the first premise, or the third premise. As a physicist who prizes the role of predictions, observation, and testing in science, I'll say that for my part, I'm not ready to let go of premise number three.

As for premise number one, it begins to feel particularly suspect and dogmatic when applied to the question of the origin of nature itself—the cosmos and its fine-tuned laws. To insist that nature and nature's laws were caused by some natural cause is, in essence, to insist that nature is somehow its own cause, which in turn is to insist that the cosmos has always existed in one form or another. That amounts to insisting that we aren't allowed to ask whether nature is or isn't eternal. As a scientist interested in searching for the truth about nature, no holds barred, I'm not keen on being told a question is off limits.

The laws of nature describe regularities in the natural order. We can ask why there are regularities in nature at all. That is, why is nature a cosmos rather than a chaos? But just as notable is the fact that the specific strengths or values of these laws are exquisitely fine tuned, at just the right values to allow the universe to form atoms, stars, and planets—conditions required for life.

Consider an example. In the moments just after the Big Bang, the universe contained only energy. According to Einstein's famous equation, $E=mc^2$, energy can transform into matter. Other laws of physics state that the result of this transformation is always composed of a particle-antiparticle pair. Antimatter is certainly real, and has been experimentally verified for many decades. What we know about it is that when a particle and its antiparticle meet, they annihilate each other and turn back into pure energy. This gives us a conundrum: all the particle-antiparticle pairs produced out of energy should have annihilated each other in the distant past, leaving nothing but energy in the universe. Thankfully, this process short-circuited early on in the history of the universe. Physicists do not understand the mechanism, but somehow, about one extra particle out of every ten billion particle-antiparticle pairs remained intact. All the rest annihilated each other and turned back into energy. All the matter we see in the universe comes from those one-in-ten-billion leftover particles.

Another remarkable outcome is that there is a one-to-one match between the number of protons and electrons in the universe. This is unexpected, since protons are 1,836 times more massive than electrons, and are completely different types of particles. Protons, being more massive, stopped forming out of energy much earlier than electrons, and yet we still end up with this essential balance in the number of particles. This leads to the overall charge neutrality of matter, since protons and electrons have equal and opposite charge.

Without neutrality of charge throughout our universe, stars and planets and life could not exist. Even a small imbalance in the number of protons and electrons would produce such a strong electric force that it would tear material structures apart. Geraint Lewis and Luke Barnes explain it this way in *A Fortunate Universe*:

> It's important to realize just how precisely electric neutrality needs to be enforced. Suppose that you were assembling Earth and got a little careless in your bookkeeping, so that for every trillion trillion trillion protons and electrons, you put into the mix, one extra electron slipped in. The combined repulsion of these extra electrons would be stronger than the attraction of gravity. The Earth would not be gravitationally bound.
>
> In fact, the same net charge (one part in 10^{36}) would preclude any gravitationally bound structure in the Universe at all. Galaxies, stars and planets would all fail to collapse under their own gravity, instead being dispersed by electromagnetic repulsion. The result: a universe of extremely diffuse gas, and not much else.[2]

Because we do have charge neutrality, stars can form through the action of gravity pulling interstellar gases together. This is a delicate process since the force of gravity is about a trillion times a trillion times a trillion (10^{36}) times weaker than the electric force between charged particles. Why is the ratio fine tuned in this way? Is there a purely natural explanation? Was intelligent design involved?

We will explore other equally impressive examples of fine tuning below. But already we have enough to ask, What could give rise to such instances of fine tuning? Can we explain fine tuning by saying that nature "just is"? If the universe with its laws were known to be eternal, we might shrug at the curious fact of fine tuning and go on. Even then such a response would leave fine tuning unexplained, but in fact we do not know that the universe is eternal. Quite the opposite. There is compelling evidence that the universe has not always existed. It had a beginning.

This scientific discovery has intriguing implications. What is known as the kalam cosmological argument comes into play. It states:

Whatever begins to exist has a cause for its existence.

The universe began to exist.

Therefore, the universe must have a cause for its existence.

What could be the cause of the universe? The universe is composed of matter, energy, space, time, and the laws of nature. These cannot bring nature into existence because they are nature; they are the very thing whose origin we are trying to explain. So, logic requires that we look for something that transcends matter, energy, space, and the laws of nature—a transcendent cause. *outside*

Some scientists hope to discover a "theory of everything" that would explain the fine-tuned properties of our universe without admitting a transcendent intelligence into the picture. Such a theory would give a natural reason why all the laws and parameters of the universe have the precise form and values they do. An overriding theory like this would serve as sort of a "master law" that dictates all the properties of nature.

Discovering such a "theory of everything" would be a triumph of understanding the physical universe. But would it give an ultimate explanation for why things are the way they are? No. It would simply introduce another cosmic question, namely, Why is the theory of everything the way it is? Why is the theory of everything life-friendly, out of all conceivable theories that might have been the case? The mystery of fine tuning would only be shifted up to a higher level.[3] So we see that a "theory of everything" would not explain away the fine tuning we observe. We also would still be faced with the question, What caused the law or laws behind the theory of everything to originate in the first place?

Something of a different order than just another theory of fundamental physics is needed to explain the origin and fine tuning of nature. The idea of a transcendent, eternal intelligence solves the unproductive regress of trying to explain nature with nature. And it provides an explanation for fine tuning. Intelligent agents fine tune things all the time. They can foresee a distant goal and arrange things in pursuit of that distant goal, however improbable it might be for chance to generate such an outcome. Random forces do not properly tune pianos, much less build the pianos. Intelligent agents do. Postulating an eternal, transcendent intelligence for the origin of the cosmos resolves the challenge of the kalam argument, avoids the problem of an infinite regress,[4] and offers an adequate explanation for cosmic fine tuning.

Fine Tuning for Life

PHYSICAL LIFE cannot exist in a vacuum. It requires building blocks made of atoms. In addition, it needs a sheltered habitat such as a planet. Life also requires a steady source of energy, as provided by a star. The list of requirements is long and growing.

Although we still have much to learn about the biochemistry of living things, science can make some definite statements concerning life in general. For one thing, we can state with confidence that there was a time when physical life didn't exist in our universe. Early in the history of the universe, no stars or planets had yet formed, and the only element was hydrogen, joined a little later by helium with traces of lithium, and beryllium.

Going back even earlier in time, only energy and subatomic particles existed. In a torrid *pas de deux*, photons of energy constantly converted into particle-antiparticle pairs, which swiftly annihilated each other in a spectacular kiss of death, releasing their rest-masses back into photons of pure energy. Under such conditions, no physical life could possibly exist.

Nor is it enough just to get past this period of matter-antimatter pyrotechnics. Life requires a safe haven to thrive. The vast reaches of space have always been inimical to life. A near-perfect vacuum pierced only by harsh radiation makes a poor nursery.

For life to exist, a shield from damaging radiation is necessary—one, however, that allows in just the sort of radiant energy friendly to life. Our planet's finely tuned atmosphere provides such a filter for life on Earth.

Life requires many other ingredients as well. These include numerous elements, the right amount of heat, liquid water, and a reasonably stable environment. These conditions are best met on Earth-like planets, as opposed to gas giants like Jupiter. Moons are also a poor substitute for

Earth-like planets—though in certain cases, the large moons of larger planets could possibly sustain simple life for portions of their history.[5]

A point of clarification: Astronomers talk about their having found "Earth-like planets" around distant stars, but we probably should use scare quotes around the term when used in that way, since to date we haven't found any planets that are like Earth in the way that makes it so special. We currently know of life on only one planet—Earth, which provides all the conditions needed to sustain life. It not only possesses all the conditions necessary for life; it's bursting with a riotous abundance and variety of life.

Before we explore our unusual planet, however, we need to return again to the earliest moments in the history of the universe. Let's take a look at what scientists have discovered about the beginning of space and time. We'll then work forward and see all that's necessary for a planet like Earth to exist.

Science Confirms a Beginning

FOR THE greater part of humanity's time on this planet, we knew next to nothing about the universe. For a long time probably the most influential account of the origin of the universe, at least in the West, came from the book of Genesis in the Bible, which describes God bringing the Earth and the cosmos into existence *ex nihilo*—that is, out of nothing. Science didn't catch up with the idea that the universe had a beginning until 1929. At that time, Edwin Hubble reported observations of distant galaxies that suggested the universe began in the finite past.

Before 1929 it was considered conventional wisdom among many astronomers that the universe was infinitely old and never had a beginning. This viewpoint wasn't based on scientific knowledge, but rather on philosophical preference. The motivations for such a preference were varied and, in some cases, complex. For some the preference was simple: if the universe never began, then one doesn't have to explain a beginning, or consider the possibility of a Creator. But discoveries in the early twentieth century provided evidence that philosophical belief in an eternal universe was wrong.

Hubble's Law

OUR CURRENT state of scientific knowledge about the universe, which most of us take for granted, is actually relatively recent in origin. When we hear the word "galaxies," we can see in our mind's eye pictures of huge spiral swarms of stars floating in the vast universe. Before the 1920s, astronomers did not know if other galaxies even existed.[6] But then more powerful telescopes revealed that nebula-looking objects lay at distances far beyond the stars of our own galaxy. They appeared to be other galaxies, far removed from own. This was remarkable in its own right, and it set the stage for an even more startling discovery.

In his observations of distant galaxies, Hubble discovered that the farther away a galaxy is, the faster it is receding from us. (See Figure 3.1.) By the way, you can't see a galaxy moving just by staring at it through a telescope—galaxies are much too far away for that. Astronomers use a "radar-gun" technique, based on the Doppler Effect. The velocity that a galaxy is moving away from us is calculated from a shift in the wavelengths of light coming towards us from the galaxy. Astronomers refer to this effect as "redshift." Hubble used this technique to estimate how fast various galaxies were moving away from ours, and at some point he noticed a pattern. The further away a galaxy was, the more redshifted its light was—that is, the faster it was moving away from us.

Hubble and others quickly realized that an expanding universe implied a universe that had a beginning. Think about it. If the universe had been expanding forever, the various bodies expanding away from each other would already be infinitely far apart, which they aren't.

Put another way, if you picture the story of the universe as a movie that you can fast forward and rewind, when you hit reverse and watch the universe regress backward in time, it shrinks smaller and smaller. But the shrinking can't go on forever. Eventually it reaches a tiny point—the beginning of the universe.

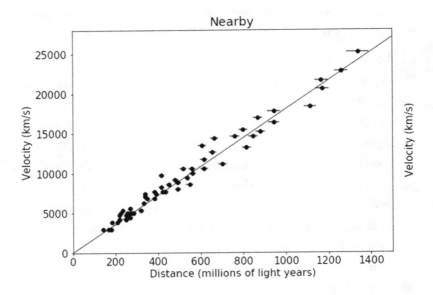

Figure 3.1. A graph illustrating Hubble's Law, showing a pattern of galaxies tending to move away from us faster the farther away they are from us, suggesting an expanding universe.

So you see, there's a good reason NASA named its extraordinary space telescope after Edwin Hubble. He cinched the case for a universal beginning, fundamentally altering how cosmologists viewed the history of the universe.

One interesting detail of this story: Einstein could have gotten there first but chose instead to explain away an implication of one of his greatest discoveries. Einstein published his momentous theory of general relativity in 1916, describing the influence of matter on space and time. His equations predicted that space must be expanding (or contracting) but could not be static. Either case (expanding or contracting) implied a universal beginning. But the weight of false philosophical inertia initially prevented Einstein from believing this clear implication of his own equations. Instead, he bowed to the prevailing consensus and penciled in a fudge factor that preserved the possibility of a static, and therefore potentially eternal, universe.

Just thirteen years later, Hubble's discovery of the expanding universe confirmed the straightforward implication of Einstein's general theory of relativity. With hindsight, Einstein described his conformity move as the biggest blunder of his life.

The theory of general relativity clarifies that the galaxies we observe to be receding from us are not flying away through space, like shrapnel from a hand grenade. Instead, they are being carried away from us by ever-expanding space itself. The correct conception is to picture the galaxies as floating in space, but with the space between galaxies continuously expanding. This perfectly explains Hubble's Law, which shows that the more space there is between galaxies, the faster they move apart.[7]

Picture a balloon that hasn't been blown up yet. Dot A on the balloon stands for Earth. Dot B is an inch away from dot A. Dot C is three inches away from dot A. Then you begin to blow up the balloon. All the dots will begin to pull away from each other, but dot C will pull away from dot A at a much faster rate than will the second dot. In this balloon illustration, the surface of the balloon is expanding. In our universe, the fabric of space itself is expanding, and with it, the universe as a whole.

Most of us are not used to the counter-intuitive idea that space can expand. We tend to think of space as a fixed emptiness between points. Within the framework of general relativity, however, space not only can expand, but it also can bend or warp, and even flow. Space is not nothing. It is definitely something. This is captured by the metaphorical language used among astronomers and physicists when we talk about the "fabric of space and time."

So let's boil all this down. The expansion of the universe as time moves forward implies that if we ran time backwards (like watching a movie in reverse), we would see the universe getting smaller and smaller, with all the galaxies moving closer together. Eventually, a finite number of years into the past, the size of the universe would go to zero. Hubble's data provided, for the first time in human history, a means to scientifically calculate the age of the universe. Observational evidence of the expansion rate of the universe allows us to calculate the time it took for the universe to expand from its beginning (when its size was essentially zero) up until today. Hubble's original data has been confirmed and refined over the decades. The consensus of data from recent observations indicates the universe began about 13.82 billion years ago.[8]

In addition, in 1970, physicists Stephen Hawking and Roger Penrose[9] showed from Einstein's equations that when the universe began, space and time began as well. A not-yet-developed theory of quantum gravity by Hawking is aimed at avoiding a true beginning of time.[10] Despite Hawking's status, his ideas suggesting the non-existence of a space-time singularity at the beginning of the universe are far from decisive. "A cosmological theorem proved by Arvind, Guth, and Vilenkin in 2003 showed that space *and* time must have a beginning under conditions of rapid inflation of the early universe," I note elsewhere. "Even if future variations of General Relativity to include quantum gravity possibly modify these conclusions, it is safe to say that the universe as we know it had a beginning out of nothing that currently exists."[11] In that case, whatever caused the beginning of the universe must transcend not only matter and energy but also space and time.

The Second Law of Thermodynamics

THERE IS additional corroborating evidence from physics that our universe is not infinitely old. One such line of evidence derives from an examination of the second law of thermodynamics. You may have heard it described as the law of entropy. The second law states that the entropy of a closed system will never decrease with time. Entropy is sometimes described as a measure of the disorder within a system. It also has a more mathematically precise definition used in thermodynamic calculations.

A simple ramification of the second law is that in a closed system, heat energy will flow from a hotter to a colder object, but not in the opposite direction. All natural thermodynamic processes are irreversible like this. Engineers can design systems that circumvent this one-way tendency of heat flow (think about refrigerators or air conditioners), but their design requires a mechanism (known as a "heat engine") and an input of energy to function. Such machines aren't closed systems, meaning the second law isn't violated with their operation.

Another ramification of the second law is that any sort of engine based on the flow of heat, such as a steam engine, or the internal combustion engines in most cars, cannot have 100% efficiency. This means that it's impossible in our universe for heat to ever be converted completely into useful work—there must always be some waste heat, or "exhaust."

The second law is so pervasive in the universe that some scientists associate it with the direction of the passage of time.[12] For example, suppose I showed you two pictures of the same egg, with one picture showing the whole egg in the shell, and the other showing it smashed on the floor. If I then asked you to place the pictures in the correct time order, you would of course say the one with the whole egg came first. We know that whole eggs can become broken, but that smashed eggs don't become whole again. The Humpty Dumpty nursery rhyme emphasizes that, even with great effort, some things can't be put together again. *boiling water*

As time progresses, the outworking of the second law will draw everything in a closed physical system toward the same temperature, *will run out of heat* meaning that useful energy (energy with which we can do work) will dwindle. This in turn suggests that the universe is gradually "winding down." Since there is strong evidence that the universe is governed by the second law, and since we still have useful energy, like sunlight, then the universe is apparently not infinitely old. Otherwise, it would have wound down to a state of maximum entropy a long, long time ago (actually infinitely long ago).

Some cosmologists have sought to sidestep the growing evidence of a cosmic beginning by postulating a kind of yo-yo universe—that is, a series of cosmic expansion and contractions, one after the other, stretching infinitely far back into the past, and in this way, restoring the idea of eternal nature. However, if the universe's expansion was slowing, with a contraction phase in the cards somewhere down the line, it could not possibly rewind in the way a movie rewinds. A contraction phase would

[handwritten annotation: bouncing universe Not infinite but like Drop a tennis ball on floor]

not reverse the law of entropy. In other words, the proverbial egg would stay broken.

This means that if our present universe were to eventually begin contracting in size under the influence of gravity, it would not return to the conditions of the early universe. Instead, the degree of entropy would continue to increase, inexorably. And if our universe was simply one phase in an infinitely old series of cosmic expansions and contractions, our universe should have reached maximum entropy an infinitely long time ago. Of course, it hasn't. This poses a significant problem for the idea of an eternal yo-yo universe wherein our universe expands and contracts, expands and contracts, over and over again through eternity. Cosmologists keen on preserving belief in an eternal cosmos have offered up various exotic, ad hoc solutions to circumvent this challenge, but the empirical support for them is slim to non-existent, and pales in comparison to the robust empirical evidence for the inexorable workings of the second law of thermodynamics.

There is a second major problem with the idea of an eternal yo-yo universe. Our best measurements currently suggest that the universe's rate of expansion will not slow or eventually reverse. Instead, the observed trend suggests that it will simply continue to expand, and even accelerate in its rate of expansion. Thus, there will be no collapse for our universe, and a rewind/rinse/repeat cycle is ruled out twice over. A true universal beginning remains the best explanation of the data.

And what a beginning! As we have seen, our knowing the expansion rate and the laws of physics allows us to infer the sequence of events immediately following the beginning. This opening act of our universe was anything but a random explosion. It was more like an orchestrated expansion, or like the opening of an elaborate "pop-up" book, in which a castle with turrets, moat, and drawbridge unfolds perfectly as the first page is opened. We turn to that next.

4. ON A KNIFE EDGE

IT CAME AS A SURPRISE TO MANY SCIENTISTS IN THE TWENTIETH century that our universe was not eternal but had a beginning. This is now widely accepted, due to the success of the theory colloquially known as the Big Bang. One implication of the Big Bang theory is that all the laws of physics were part of the universe at the moment of its beginning. The term "big bang" makes it sound like a chaotic affair, something akin to a bomb going off. But it was anything but a haphazard explosion. In order to obtain the unfolding masterpiece of our universe, specific values of the constants of nature had to be just so. Otherwise, stars, planets, and our life-friendly periodic table of elements would not have formed. Our universe would have been an uninhabitable waste of space with relatively simple particles from top to bottom.

This isn't controversial. It's the settled view in the field. These laws and parameters have precise values within an extremely narrow range out of all possible values. Calculations show that this set of physical values could not deviate from its knife-edge balance without making the entire universe unlivable.[1] This is referred to as the anthropic (human-centered) principle.

It is a remarkable feature of our universe, and yet some have suggested it shouldn't surprise us. After all, if the constants of nature did not have values that allowed for life, we wouldn't be here to notice it. There is more than one problem with this explanation. The first is a logical problem. What's needed here is a causal explanation for fine tuning. What's offered instead is a necessary condition for our noticing fine tuning. We can think of all sorts of other situations where we would never accept this sort of answer.

firing squad All miss

Consider an illustration: Two convicts have been sentenced to death. The firing squad raise their rifles and fire. The two convicts blink. They're unharmed! There are bullet patterns in the wall behind each of them, in the shape of a human. Each bullet has missed flesh by a hair. "Wonderful!" cries the first convict. "They must have been told to scare us but spare us." The second convict shakes his head. "You're jumping to a false conclusion by supposing we were intended to live. Don't you see? If the bullets hadn't missed us, we wouldn't even be alive to notice our good luck."[2] That's just the sort of wrongheaded reasoning we encounter when someone shrugs at cosmic fine tuning and says, "Well of course there's fine tuning. If not, we wouldn't be here to remark on our good luck."

A second problem: Yes, the values of the laws and constants of nature must be in a range that allows us to exist if we're going to be around to notice our good fortune, but the surprising thing is how *narrow* this range of possible values turns out to be.[3] For example, we could imagine a universe in which the range of values that would allow for life is broad. In such a make-believe universe, changing any one of the parameters by a factor of ten or so would not destroy the ability of the universe to support life. This hypothetical situation is very different from what we actually find. In reality, many fundamental parameters could not change by more than a fraction of a percent without making our universe totally uninhabitable.

So yes, if we are to be here to observe our good fortune, the parameters must fall in a range that allows observers to exist; but our being here to discover fine tuning doesn't require that those parameters be balanced on a knife edge. Since they are, we have an additional reason to suspect, as the distinguished astronomer Fred Hoyle has famously said, that a "super-intellect has monkeyed with physics."[4] Hoyle, by the way, wasn't religious, and even resisted the idea of a cosmic beginning. It would seem that he was driven by the evidence alone to concede that fine tuning strongly suggests a cosmic fine tuner.

CAN'T be AN Accident

A Fine-Tuning Showcase

AN ORCHESTRA with its musical instruments out of tune can't play a symphony worth hearing. A universe whose parameters are out of tune can't play a symphony that sustains life. Fortunately for us, the parameters of our universe are finely tuned to allow for life. Let's briefly consider a few of these. We will consider why life requires fine tuning in each case, and look at just how finely tuned each aspect needs to be to allow for life.

A Just-Right Expansion Rate

Life requires stars and galaxies. But if the early universe had expanded too quickly, matter would have spread out too thinly before gravity could coalesce to form galaxies. On the other hand, if the expansion rate had been too slow, gravity would have re-collapsed the universe into a mess of black holes. In either case, life would not be possible.

How finely tuned did the early expansion rate need to be? Scientists estimate[5] that the expansion rate had to be tuned to within one part in 10^{60}. Another way of thinking about this is that the odds of arriving at it randomly are no better than one chance in 10^{60}. How unlikely is this? The number of grains of sand on all the beaches and in all the deserts on Earth has been estimated at about 10^{19}. If you had to pick out, blindfolded and at random, the one invisibly marked grain of sand from all the grains of sand on Earth, and you manage it on the first try, then someone hides it again among all the sand on Earth, and you get lucky and pick it a second time, and then a third time, the odds of that are one chance in 10^{57}, still about a thousand times better odds than getting the expansion rate of the universe just right by chance.

True, this fine-tuning value is affected by the theory of cosmological inflation. Rather than a cosmic principle of rising prices, this inflation theory asserts that an ultra-fast expansion briefly occurred very early in the history of the universe. The temporary ultra-rapid expansion of space is said to iron out the need for an initial finely tuned expansion rate. This doesn't remove the mystery, however, because the process of inflation itself has to be finely tuned. The conditions for inflation to start and stop at the right time, and to expand the universe by just the right amount, introduce further fine-tuning restraints.[6] Astrophysicist Rodney Holder remarks on the specifications needed for inflation to accomplish its goal: "The fine-tuning required by inflationary models is a serious drawback since inflation was meant to explain fine-tuning!"[7] Philosopher of science C. D. McCoy concludes, "In particular, when one views fine-tuning problems as 'likelihood' problems, there is no convincing proof that inflation has solved them at all."[8]

Dark Energy Hits the Accelerator

A surprising aspect of the story of the expansion of the universe was discovered in 1998. When first studying the expanding universe, astronomers expected that the rate of expansion would slow down with time. This slowing of the outward expansion would naturally occur, it was thought, due to the mutual gravitational attraction among all the matter in the universe. However, sensitive measurements of the speed at which very distant galaxies are receding from us suggest that the rate of expansion began to accelerate about seven billion years ago.[9]

Measurements suggest that the expansion rate indeed began to slow initially, but then the rate began to accelerate. Imagine if you threw a ball straight up into the air, and after slowing for a bit in its upward trajectory, it suddenly began to pick up speed and accelerated faster and faster out of sight. You might be surprised, to say the least. The only way this could possibly happen is if some unseen force propelled the ball up and away from Earth.

Currently the leading theory for an accelerating expansion rate is that space is imbued with a sort of cosmic repulsion, or "dark energy." This energy increases in strength as the size of the spatial universe increases. Although some scientists were initially skeptical of the data leading to the conclusion of dark energy, its validity has become more widely accepted. In 2011, the leading scientists who measured the accelerating universe received the Nobel Prize in Physics for their discovery.[10]

In comparison to the amount of normal energy and matter in the universe, the estimated amount of dark energy is huge, totaling sixteen times the amount of normal matter and energy combined.[11] The identity and nature of this dark energy, however, is one of the major unsolved problems in physics.

Interestingly, scientists have found that the amount of dark energy also demands remarkable fine tuning. In order to explain dark energy within the context of existing theories of physics, its strength would need to have been fine tuned to one part in 10^{120} in order for life to be possible.[12] To give some idea of how big a number that is, there are an estimated 10^{80} atoms in the entire visible universe. The number 10^{120} is a trillion times a trillion times a trillion times ten thousand times (10^{40}) bigger than that.

"Absurdly Low Entropy"

Oxford mathematician and physicist Roger Penrose has drawn attention to the remarkable fact that our universe began in a very smoothly distributed state of matter, energy, and space-time. He describes these initial conditions as a state of "absurdly low entropy."[13] The second law of thermodynamics states that the entropy of the universe must (and does) increase with time. The initial low entropy of our universe allows the second law to function such that energy can produce useful work and sustain life. In addition, entropy increases as gravity pulls together primordial gases in the universe to form stars. The "absurdly low entropy" of our universe in the beginning is required so that galaxies and stars could eventually form, rather than a mess of black holes.

To determine just how special the initial entropy state of the Big Bang was, Penrose calculated the probability of randomly obtaining this initial low-entropy state. He determined that the chance of obtaining a universe with initial conditions as special as ours is only one part in 10 to the 10^{123}. That second number has so many zeroes after it that if we picture each zero as a centimeter wide, the full number would stretch across the entire visible universe trillions of times over, and even then would only just barely be getting started. Mind-blowingly long odds, in other words. Missing these precise conditions would lead to a completely uninhabitable universe.

Evidence from the Past

In studying the history of a civilization or of Earth itself, scientists are faced with a difficulty—the past often lies buried and is sometimes completely erased by geological forces. Not so with the study of the universe. Looking deep into the universe is like watching video footage recorded millions and billions of years ago.

From our vantage point within the Milky Way, astronomers are privileged to have a remarkably clear view of other galaxies. With the use of large telescopes we can see myriads of galaxies at a huge range of distances from us, with some galaxies thousands of times farther away than others. The farther astronomers look out into space, the farther back in time they observe. Time and distance correlate in this way because light travels at a finite speed. The speed of light is about 186,000 miles per second. A light year is the distance light travels in one year—about six trillion miles. This means that when we look at objects out in the universe, we observe them a number of years in the past equal to their distance from us in light years.

For example, the constellation Orion is about 1,500 light years away, so if you observe it tonight, you are seeing how it was 1,500 years ago. Orion is composed of stars and nebulae within our own galaxy. Viewing other galaxies allows astronomers to look much further into the past. The Andromeda galaxy is our nearest galaxy neighbor, but it's a whopping 2.5 million light years away, so we're witnessing that galaxy as it existed 2.5 million years ago. There are galaxies we have witnessed through our most powerful telescopes that are fully billions of light years away, so we are witnessing them as they existed billions of years ago.

Due to the ongoing expansion of the universe, the current positions of more distant galaxies are even farther away than they appear to us now. Also, there's a maximum distance that astronomers can see, related to the age of the universe. Because the universe began about 13.8 billion years ago, the maximum distance that light can have travelled in that time is 13.8 billion light years. This distance defines what is called the *cosmic horizon,* and it forms a limit to how far away it is possible to view anything out in the universe. Our current best understanding, though, is that there is more universe beyond the cosmic horizon. How could the universe have expanded faster than the speed of light? An implication of Einstein's general theory of relativity is that the expansion of space itself isn't limited by the speed of light. Yes, mind-bending, but there you have it. And while building bigger telescopes may let you resolve more detail, they still won't let you see stars beyond the cosmic horizon, simply because the light from beyond the cosmic horizon hasn't had time to reach us.

Another problem is that in the earliest phases of the universe, stars had not yet formed. So when we use powerful telescopes to look deep enough into space on our side of the cosmic horizon, we're looking at a time when there were no stars to see.

Also, the farther away something is, the more space there is to have stretched, which in turn stretches visible light into the infrared region, a wavelength invisible to even the most powerful of ordinary telescopes. A successor to the orbiting Hubble Space Telescope, the James Webb Space Telescope (set to launch in 2021), will be able to sensitively image infrared light to make observations of highly red-shifted objects in the early universe. In addition, other types of instruments will allow observations of even earlier eras of the universe. One such observation picks up a microwave signal originating long before the universe became filled with the light of stars.

Cosmic Microwave Background Radiation

STARTING FROM the Big Bang, as the universe expanded, it cooled. Its hot, dense initial state consisted of elementary particles and energy. These eventually cooled enough to form simple atomic nuclei and electrons. Continued expansion then gradually cooled this "plasma" (ionized gas) to the point where electrons could combine with protons and heavier nuclei. The result was the formation of stable atoms of hydrogen and helium, the two most common elements in our universe.

This event is termed *recombination.* It is estimated to have occurred about 380,000 years after the Big Bang. At that time, the background temperature of the entire universe was a still blistering 3,000 kelvin[14] (4,940 Fahrenheit), which is roughly half the surface temperature of our sun. The recombination event produced a signature detectable today, known as cosmic microwave background radiation.

Before recombination, matter consisted of positively charged nuclei and negatively charged electrons. Such a mix of charged particles, called an ionized plasma, caused the universe to be opaque to light. But once neutral atoms of hydrogen and helium formed, the universe became transparent, and radiation could travel freely.

The unique signature of this event was the emission of a well-known spectrum of radiation called blackbody radiation. All hot, dense objects (such as the heating element in an oven) emit this type of radiation. The radiation emitted during recombination had a spectrum (meaning its intensity vs. wavelength) that would have peaked in the near-infrared. However, the universe has continuously expanded from the time of re-combination until now, growing in size by about a factor of 1,100. As a result, the wavelengths of the infrared radiation emitted during recom-bination also grew by the same factor as the universe expanded. The ex-pansion shifted the peak of the spectrum from the near-infrared into the microwave region.

Bell lab scientists Arno Penzias and Robert Wilson discovered this radiation in 1965. They were working with a sensitive microwave an-tenna when they picked up a signal coming from every direction in the sky. Analyzing it, they determined that it matched the predicted cosmic microwave background radiation. One way to think of this radiation is as a remnant heat glow from the hot, early history of our universe.

The 3,000 kelvin temperature at the time of recombination was ex-pected to have cooled to about five degrees above absolute zero in the current era.[15] This cooling occurred as the universe expanded about 1,100 times in size since the time of recombination.[16] In agreement with this prediction, when the background radiation was discovered, its spectrum was found to correspond to a temperature of 2.73 kelvin.

Repeated measurements of this radiation, using balloon-based and satellite instruments, have verified that the microwave background exactly matches the theoretically predicted spectrum. These measurements provide strong evidence confirming the hot Big Bang model for the early history of our universe.

It would be good at this point to pause and reflect on this accomplishment. Humans developing a verifiable scientific model for the origin of the universe is nothing short of amazing. The origin event itself happened long before the Earth even came into existence. And yet scientists working with the Big Bang model were able to make detailed predictions, as early as 1948, of radiation in the universe, which subsequent discoveries confirmed.

Sophisticated satellite measurements of the microwave background radiation across the whole sky revealed that its intensity was remarkably uniform in all directions. But such uniformity was problematic. Scientists knew that unless very small non-uniformities rippled through the background radiation, no galaxies could have ever formed. The uniformity of the background radiation is proportional to the uniformity of ordinary matter in the early universe (long before any stars or galaxies formed). For galaxies to eventually form by gravitational attraction of matter around denser regions, non-uniformities of about one part in 100,000 would be necessary.

More sensitive satellite measurements in the early 1990s showed that the microwave background radiation did in fact show the required variations across the sky.[17] These significant observations provided additional confirmation that the Big Bang model is valid.

A Universe Without Center or Edge?

TWO COMMON questions arise when students first hear about the Big Bang theory: "Where did the Big Bang occur?" and "What is the universe expanding into?"

It's natural for us to ask such questions if we think of the Big Bang as an explosion of primordial matter and energy occurring somewhere in an empty universe. When we look out into the universe from Earth, we see other galaxies in all directions moving away from us. We might then conclude that we are in the center of the universe. However, the recession of galaxies away from us is not due to their movement *through* space. As explained earlier, it's the expansion of space itself that carries the galaxies apart. And all of space is expanding, so observers in any galaxy would observe the same thing—distant galaxies moving away from them.

So, if we're not in the center of the universe, where is the center? One way this question is answered is to say that the universe has no center. One could also say that every point in the universe used to be in the same location, when the universe first began. In the beginning, the universe had almost zero initial size, meaning the location of the Big Bang was everywhere.

The idea of the universe having no center is akin to the surface of the Earth having no center. No geographical point can be considered the center of the Earth's surface. Now, of course, we realize that planet Earth has a center point lying deep down inside its core, but to get there we would have to leave the surface of the Earth and travel about 4,000 miles straight down below the surface. Likewise, the universe could have a center, but to get there, we'd have to leave the three-dimensional "surface" of the universe and travel in a higher dimension perpendicular to that surface an unknown distance. This analogy maps on to our universe if three-dimensional space, out beyond the cosmic horizon, gradually curves back around on itself, in what is known as positive curvature. (The mental picture of this application of higher-dimensional geometry is hard to envision, but it's fun to try.) The curvature of space in our universe is predicted in Einstein's theory of general relativity, and could be curved in three different ways, depending upon the overall mass density of the universe.

Measurements of the variations in the cosmic microwave background radiation indicate that the local curvature of space out to the cosmic horizon is flat.[18] But beyond that, we can't say for sure. I imagine that it eventually curves back on itself, but with such a slight curvature that it looks flat from our perspective, much like the landscape in Indiana. Here, the local topography can look pretty flat, even though it's actually curved as part of the surface of our planetary globe. In a similar way, current observations do not rule out the possibility that far beyond the cosmic horizon, the universe could curve back on itself and close, like the surface of a sphere. This means that, hypothetically, if you took off in a spaceship in one direction, and kept travelling long enough, you would come back home without ever turning around.

If we return to the question of what the universe is expanding into, some cosmologists simply divert the question by stating that all we can say is that the length scale of the universe is continuously increasing. (I admit that's not a very satisfying answer.) Without any observational evidence for a higher-dimensional space into which the universe might be expanding, it's probably best to just say that the universe (which is everything we can observe) is simply getting bigger, with the space between distant galaxies constantly being stretched out.

Dark Matter and Its Effects within the Universe

WE DISCUSSED above the concept of dark energy. It's also theorized that the universe contains a significant amount of dark matter. How does it make its presence felt? Dark matter, like normal matter, is said to exert a gravitational pull on all other matter.

One way astronomers deduce dark matter's presence is when they measure the rotational rates of spiral galaxies. Observations reveal that such galaxies have a higher density of stars in their central regions. Based on that, we'd expect that the velocities of stars orbiting around their galactic centers should decrease the farther from the center one looked. In this way, spiral galaxies should rotate somewhat like a giant solar system. For example, the planets farthest from the sun move with much slower velocities than those closer in.

One fun part of doing science comes when nature surprises us, and that's what happened with the orbital velocities of stars in spiral galaxies. The stars farther from the galactic center do not move slower than those closer to the center—in contrast to what astronomers expected.

When faced with such a discrepancy between theory and observation, scientists are faced with a choice: either abandon the theory, or look for another explanation to reconcile the data with the current theory. Since the theory in question here is the venerable and well-verified Newtonian theory of gravity, scientists were reluctant to abandon or even modify it. (Newtonian gravity has been experimentally verified in the lab and throughout the solar system, a range of over twelve orders of magnitude in distance). The alternative solution, then, was to propose the existence of dark matter. In sufficient abundance, unseen dark matter could explain the discrepancy between theory and observations of galactic rotation.

Dark matter is called "dark" because it does not interact with light, as normal matter does. It still attracts other matter by the gravitational force, however. Therefore, a sufficient quantity of dark matter in and around a galaxy could modify the expected fall-off in rotational velocities. Dark matter could cause the outermost stars in a galaxy to orbit as fast as the inner ones.

Astronomers estimate that the amount of dark matter required is about five times more than the amount of normal matter.[19] Additional evidence for the amount of unseen dark matter comes from observations of gravitational lensing. This phenomenon results from the warping of space by mass, as predicted by Einstein's theory of general relativity. In gravitational lensing, the light from distant galaxies is focused by the mass of a galaxy cluster situated between the distant galaxies and Earth.

Even a modest-sized star, such as our sun, can and does bend light from distant stars as their light passes close by the sun on the way to Earth. In a similar fashion, light from a distant galaxy bends when travelling past a galaxy cluster on its way to Earth. The degree of bending is proportional to the amount of matter present in the intervening galaxy cluster. The mass of the cluster can be estimated from the amount of starlight seen in it—and it doesn't add up. More matter must be present in the cluster to accomplish the observed degree of bending. Therefore, scientists again postulate dark matter to make up the difference.

Scientists realize that dark matter also played an important role in the history and formation of galaxies. In the early universe, before galaxies formed, the gravitational pull of dark matter accentuated the gravity of normal matter. The result was that small density variations in the distribution of matter had sufficient gravity to clump primordial gases together. In this way, vast conglomerations of matter formed into individual galaxies and clusters of galaxies.[20] In short, without dark matter, galaxies might have never formed, and we wouldn't be here either.[21]

The Mystery of Dark Matter and Dark Energy

WE STILL aren't sure what dark matter actually is, except that it's not just non-luminous normal matter (such as burnt-out stars or stray planets).[22] A popular candidate for dark matter is an unknown type of weakly interacting massive particle (WIMP, for short). Several experimental research groups have built detectors to try to capture and characterize these particles.[23] Initial results from some experiments have narrowed the range of possible dark matter characteristics, but have not yet obtained a positive identification of dark matter.[24] One exotic idea is that dark matter is composed of a particle which partially exists in higher dimensions. Its gravitational force would still noticeably manifest in our dimensions, but it would interact only very weakly with electromagnetic radiation, making it dark.[25]

Dark energy is even less understood than dark matter. The leading idea at the moment is that it's a form of the cosmological constant. This constant is a re-instatement of the "fudge factor" Einstein penciled into his general relativity equation in order to cancel out the expansion of space. But the dark energy version would *contribute* to the expansion, rather than canceling it out.[26] A major astronomical observational effort known as the Dark Energy Survey is currently underway, with the goal of clarifying the nature of dark energy.[27]

Although scientists continue to investigate the mysterious nature of dark matter and dark energy, researchers think they have determined the relative amount of each in the universe. In terms of percentages, the total mass-energy census of the universe breaks down as follows: normal matter and energy, 4.6% (this is what all the stars and planets are made of); dark matter, 23.2%; and dark energy, 72.2%.[28] The fine tuning related to the amount of dark energy, mentioned earlier as an incredible one part out of 10^{120}, has led physicist Paul Davies to conclude, "The cliché that 'life is balanced on a knife-edge' is a staggering understatement in this case."[29]

The combined total gives just enough mass-energy to achieve what is known as the "critical density." The overall curvature of space in the universe is determined by the density of mass-energy throughout the universe (including dark matter and energy). Its value turns out to be the critical density, which is the amount required to make the geometry of the observable universe flat.[30] The fact that the geometry of the observable universe is flat simply means that all the rules of geometry you might have learned in high school—such as "the interior angles of any triangle add up to 180 degrees"—apply even for triangles drawn on an inter-galactic scale.

I suppose that's comforting to the mathematically inclined among us, but the benefits of a flat observable universe extend beyond geometry. Our cosmic home might never have become habitable without it.[31] The universal-scale features discussed in this chapter, including inflation, dark matter and energy, and the resulting flat geometry combine in a way that has allowed stars and galaxies to form and provide a stable backdrop for life.

In the next chapter, we will consider more of the ancient story of the cosmos and its connection to our own human story.

5. Vast and Ancient

THE GREAT SIZE AND AGE OF OUR UNIVERSE, MEASURED IN BIL-
lions of years and billions of light years, stir in many of us a feeling
of awe, of standing before some great mystery. Equally awe-inspiring is
the fact that we live in a universe that has revealed so much about itself—both its distant reaches and its ancient past. Let's move forward
now from the Big Bang to explore the subsequent stages of this great
cosmic drama.

From Gas to Galaxies

AFTER RECOMBINATION (the event that gave rise to the microwave background radiation), nearly all the matter in the universe consisted of the
elements hydrogen and helium. The properties of nuclear physics, the
relative masses of the proton and the neutron, and the expansion rate of
the early universe allow scientists to estimate how much of each element
should exist today. Their calculations match the observed measurements
of 76% hydrogen and 24% helium, by mass. This match between actual
observations and theoretical predictions provides additional confirmation of the Big Bang model and its conclusion that our universe had a
beginning.

After helium nuclei formed via nuclear fusion in the early universe,
the temperature of the universe had cooled too much to fuse heavier elements, except for a very small amount of lithium. During this period
the universe, consisting of a uniform mixture of hydrogen and helium,
expanded in silent darkness. The coming of light would have to wait
for gravity's slow contraction of matter into the denser spheres of stars.
These dark ages, as they're called, lasted about 200 million years before
the first stars gave forth their light[2] and began to fuse together heavier
elements inside their stellar furnaces. The measured ratio of helium to

hydrogen helps govern the production rate of heavier elements via fusion in the cores of stars. When these stars eventually explode, they expel most of their mass back into space, seeding it with heavier elements. (More on this in a bit.)

Galaxies, islands of hundreds of billions of stars, had coalesced by about 500 million years after the Big Bang. Within one of the hundreds of billions of galaxies in our universe, a spiral galaxy we call the Milky Way was eventually brought into existence, and within the Milky Way our sun and its planets, including Earth. The primordial hydrogen and helium, formed within just a few minutes after the Big Bang, and salted with the heavier elements produced in the cores of stars, made for a just-right mixture to allow Earth to sustain life.

The mass density of the universe also appears to be fine tuned to allow for a habitable universe. In the previous chapter, we saw that the expansion rate of the universe must be finely tuned in order for the universe to neither collapse nor fizzle. The mass density affects this finely tuned expansion rate via the force of gravity. Too much mass density, all other things being equal, and it would have collapsed in a big crunch; too little and matter would have dispersed too quickly without ever forming stars and galaxies. Fortunately, the mass density, along with other factors affecting the expansion rate, were just right to make life possible.

Why So Old and Vast?

WE MAY have wondered at times, "Why is the universe so old?" A human lifespan, or even the span of time that humanity has lived on Earth, is utterly dwarfed by the estimated age of the universe, 13.8 billion years. This seems like an awfully long time. However, it can help our understanding to put things into perspective. The most common stars in the universe are ones less massive than our sun, the so-called red dwarfs. Stars in this category have anticipated lifespans of one hundred billion years or more.[3] From that perspective, the age of the universe is so short that they have barely had time to attain adolescence.

But some may still wonder, If God is particularly interested in humans, why design a universe in which so many billions of years pass by
before humans even come on the scene? A good theological question,
to which there is a good theological answer: To the eternal God, such
stretches of time are not daunting. God is the master of time. To him a
day is as a thousand years, and a thousand years—or a million or a billion—is as a day, or a watch in the night. He is the maker of our space-
time continuum, not a slave to it. And yes, he loves us and delighted in
our creation, but he was not lonely or needy for us in our absence. He
is self-sufficient, emotionally and otherwise. Additionally, the maker of
Triune the cosmos may have many purposes for this universe. Neither theism in
general nor a biblical worldview in particular rules that out.

This book is focused on scientific evidence in origins science, but
I mention this theological explanation for the great age of the universe
because it addresses a question that would occur to many thoughtful
people, and because atheists often insist that if the God of the Bible really existed, he wouldn't have waited several billion years before making
humans. "God wouldn't have done it that way," they insist. But that theological argument responds to a strawman version of theism, not to the
God we actually find depicted in the Abrahamic religions.

Science also offers an answer to the question. To explain the great
age of the universe, we turn again to the laws of physics and astronomy.
They inform us that it takes a long time to produce the elements necessary for life, such as carbon, oxygen, and iron, from nuclear fusion in the
cores of massive stars. Given our laws of physics, the process of stellar
nucleosynthesis is about the only way these life-essential elements can be
formed naturally through the unfolding of our universe.

Yes, one can hypothesize a cosmic designer who opts for a universe
in which these heavier elements are merely called into being, presto
change. But if one is invoking aesthetic or theological arguments against
the idea of a cosmic designer, it's far from obvious that a presto-chango
approach to generating and distributing the heavy elements is superior

to the grand and stately unfolding of the cosmos revealed by modern cosmology, aesthetically or otherwise.

The same goes for the great size of the universe. It may turn out that the great mass of our universe is also part of the finely tuned unfolding of a life-allowing universe. The jury is still out on how much the total mass of the universe could have varied from what it is without spoiling the finely tuned unfolding that allowed for our habitable planet. But if one is thinking of an all-wise, all-powerful deity, one could imagine this divine architect snapping our sun and its planets into existence in a much smaller universe, a cozier cosmos that testifies very bluntly that humans are the center of the action and the apple of the maker's eye. Why not go that route? Some, after all, have argued that if God was the cause of the cosmos, and if humanity was his primary concern, surely he wouldn't have made billions of other stars and galaxies.

Would this younger, smaller universe be a better universe, even just from a human perspective? Not necessarily, for the vast reaches of our actual universe serve another human purpose. The vast size and wonder of the universe can affirm for us that the grandeur of its maker must be greater still. Stars have always attracted our attention and stirred our sense of wonder, and now we know that their light only reaches us across distances of interstellar space unimaginably vast. Their shining but un-reachable beauty may resonate with a longing in our hearts for some-thing beyond ourselves, unattainable by our own efforts.

Now, if one objects that this is a theological answer, recall that it's an answer to a theological question. As a physicist I am very much at home focusing on the scientific evidence of fine tuning and the Big Bang, but in my experience, questions of this sort often arise and it's fitting to pause and engage them.

Once a massive star has produced heavy elements in its core, some-thing else must happen or else this treasure trove of heavy elements would forever be locked up deep inside massive stellar remnants. The solution is a supernova explosion. This spectacular fireworks display, the final act of a massive star's life, spreads heavy elements throughout interstellar space. The heavy elements then become part of interstellar nebulae, which may eventually collapse into the next generation of stars.

The saga of supernova explosions and subsequent star formation must continue for a few stellar generations until enough heavy elements build up in the interstellar nebulae. When this happens, these nebulae can form new star systems with not only gas giant planets (like Jupiter and Saturn), but also planets with solid surfaces, like Earth. Astronomers estimate that in order to obtain sufficient quantities of the heavier elements needed for a planet to be able to sustain life, in a habitable region of a habitable galaxy such as the Milky Way, the overall time required is several billion years.[4] — 9–10 billion yrs

With regards to life, supernovae are a double-edge sword. They are necessary to enrich the interstellar nebulae with sufficient heavy elements for life, but they also pose a significant health hazard for living things. A single supernova explosion releases enough energy to outshine all the other stars in its host galaxy combined. Such a powerful source of radiation exploding in the vicinity of Earth well might sterilize the planet.

For this reason, life (especially advanced life) could not have survived for long until the rate of supernova explosions in the galaxy decreased. This naturally occurs as a galaxy ages, due to the diminishing supply of available interstellar gases necessary to form massive stars.

So the unfolding universe needs an estimated several billion years to form rocky, Earth-like planets in habitable regions, using the heavy elements spread throughout space by supernova explosions. Advanced life (multicellular organisms) did not appear on Earth until about a half billion years ago (about 13.3 billion years after the Big Bang). By this time, the galactic supernova rate had settled down enough so as to not overdose Earth with lethally potent supernovae radiation from nearby stars.

Overall, our study of the universe reveals that given the laws of physics, Earth may have come into existence at close to the earliest possible time after the Big Bang origin event to sustain life.

In order for life to thrive on our planet, the universe also couldn't have been much older than it was when Earth formed. As the universe ages, its ability to produce new stars diminishes, so in an older universe, only the long-lived red dwarf stars would remain. These smaller stars are cooler than our sun, and that affects where life-sustaining planets can orbit. A planet would have to orbit closer to a small star in order for the temperature to be in the right range to keep water liquid on the planet's surface. The problem with this solution is that the planet would become tidally locked as it orbited. Our moon, for example, has become tidally locked so that it always keeps the same face towards Earth. A tidally locked planet would have one side always facing its host star, and the opposite side always facing the darkness. One side freezes while the other side bakes.

Another problem with red-dwarf host stars, one widely recognized by astrobiologists, is that their planets would be subject to more energetic outbursts of radiation. The combined effects of temperature extremes and ionizing radiation would render the habitability of these planets nearly zero.

Also, if our universe were much older than it is, the abundance of radioactive elements would not be ideal. Radioactive elements are produced in supernova explosions, which become less frequent as the universe ages. These radioactive elements have long but limited lifespans, and they decay away as the universe ages. The diminished rate of supernova explosions can't adequately resupply them. Within our planet, radioactive elements produce heat from their decay processes. They are responsible for keeping the interior of our planet warm enough to sustain a molten iron core, a condition necessary for Earth's life-protecting magnetic field. In addition, the heat from radioactive decay drives plate tectonics, an essential feature for recycling materials in the Earth's crust in order to maintain the Earth's habitability.[5]

So we find that our planet didn't have all the time in the world to get the biosphere show on the road. There is a finite window of opportunity for a living planet such as Earth. Neither too early nor too late in the unfolding cosmic drama would do. From both scientific and theological considerations, then, the age of the universe and the timing of the origins of the Earth and life are all consistent with the concept of a cosmic designer with a keen interest in human beings.

The Multiverse Escape Clause

SOME SCIENTISTS have postulated that our universe represents only one of many (say 10^{500}) universes. All these together comprise the so-called multiverse. The unprovable concept of a multiverse has offered an escape to those unwilling to see fine tuning as evidence of intelligent design. With a multiverse, the bio-friendly fine tuning of our universe's parameters is thought to arise as a random outcome from among a large sample of universes.[6]

The physical parameters of each universe in the multiverse are assumed to span all possible values, with most yielding uninhabitable universes. One crucial part of this speculation is some physical mechanism for producing such universes, but no such mechanism is known. As physicist Paul Davies states, "Multiverse devotees... accept a package of wonders, including a universe-generating mechanism."[7]

So, according to this explanation, fine tuning might seem to suggest that the universe was designed with creatures like us in mind, that we are an intended culmination of some grand cosmic drama; but no, it's all just dumb luck. Does the multiverse hypothesis, then, effectively nullify this appearance of purpose and design? Even a multiverse is a natural phenomenon, requiring an explanation for its origin. Natural things are not eternal, nor are they ultimately self-creating.

For the sake of argument, though, suppose a multiverse did exist, with our universe being just one universe among a myriad of universes. Suppose also that we could study the properties of this multiverse. Would we find it utterly random and haphazard? The trends found throughout our universe reveal that order and specificity are the rule, not the exception. As astronomer Hugh Ross put it, "The more accurately and extensively astronomers measure the universe, the more finely

Trend line

tuned they discover it to be."[8] What reason do we have to suppose that this trend would not continue into the hypothesized multiverse and multiverse generator, if observations could ever probe their existence and properties? The evidence and line of reasoning we have seen so far suggests that if (and this is a very big "if") we could investigate a multiverse, even more evidence for fine tuning would be found within the overarching physics of such a multiverse, providing further support for the thesis of design.

A Chance for Life?

In a later chapter we'll explore the origin of life from the perspective of information theory. But if the conclusions reached there are correct, we would need an unimaginably great number of universes in a multiverse to successfully argue that life likely would arise in at least one of them by chance. One solution has been to suggest that the proposed multiverse contains an infinite number of universes.

With an infinite number of universes and infinite variety among them, we now have a situation where just about anything can happen, including the long-odds chance origin of the first life. Think of someone rolling a thousand dice trying to get them all to come up sixes by chance. Good luck with that! But if you have an infinite number of tries, you will succeed. An infinite number of tries has a way of taming even the longest odds. Similarly, if each universe in the multiverse is a try at the chance origin of life, and the multiverse has an infinite number of tries, success is guaranteed.

However, the moment we invoke an infinite multiverse, we find ourselves mired in some sticky logical problems. First is the logical impossibility of an infinite number of any physical objects, be they universes or books.[9] What's impossible about a physical infinity? Let's consider books, which are easier to imagine than universes. An infinite number of books in a library would mean that you could remove any number of books and still have the same number as before. That's a mathematical contradiction and, therefore, impossible.

Also, assembling an infinite number of items would take an infinite amount of time, requiring a physical existence stretching infinitely far into the past. This would again presuppose the eternal existence of the natural, which contradicts the nature of nature.

But perhaps the most fundamental problem with supposing an infinite multiverse is that the anything-could-happen premise is self-defeating. If everything could have happened in such a multiverse, then this would include the origin of a universe-destroying machine or even a multiverse-destroying machine. But since we obviously haven't been destroyed by such a machine, the argument for "anything could happen" is false (not to mention ridiculous).

So we see that positing an infinite multiverse to explain the origin of life and our wildly improbable universe entangles one in multiple absurdities. Mathematician and philosopher of physics Bruce Gordon concludes, "By providing an all-too-easy explanation for anything that has happened or may happen, the multiverse ends up explaining nothing at all."[10]

One imaginative cosmologist, Edward Harrison,[11] suggested that our universe was created by intelligent aliens who exist in another universe (if this isn't advocating intelligent design, I don't know what is). Harrison suggests that new universes could be created by an advanced race of beings. In his review of this idea, Rodney Holder comments that the physics involved in such an idea are speculative, and it "smacks of desperation." I would agree. It smacks of a desperate attempt to avoid the conclusion of a cosmic designer.[12]

Gordon addresses another problem with appeals to an infinite multiverse. If the hard problems of the origin of life and consciousness are "solved" by supposing they happened in our universe thanks to the creative powers of the hypothesized multiverse-generating machine, then what becomes of science? The scientific enterprise has been reduced to saying, "If the natural forces of our universe can't explain it, we'll suppose it just happened as a random outcome of an unknowable process acting in a meta-universe." A "random miracle," as Gordon puts it,[13] is arguably less scientific than a theistic miracle. The former has no identifiable cause, mechanism, or rationality; the latter allows the identification of both cause, means, and rationale.

Summary and Reflection

Insights from modern physics and observations of distant galaxies reveal that space is expanding, or being stretched out. As we run the proverbial tape of the universe in reverse, we reach a point where time, space, and all matter and energy had a beginning at a finite time in the past. The implication is that whatever caused the beginning of the universe must transcend the universe. The universe cannot have brought itself into being, so the cause of the universe lies beyond or outside of the universe. The cause or maker of the universe must have pre-programmed all the laws of physics at the moment of its beginning, and have done it in just such a way as to provide the physical conditions necessary for life to exist in the cosmos.

The Big Bang model describes the unfolding of the universe out of nothing, with its remarkable degree of fine tuning for life. Nobel laureate Arno Penzias ably summarized the wider implications of those findings. "Astronomy leads us to a unique event," he commented, "a universe which was created out of nothing, one with the very delicate balance needed to provide exactly the conditions required to permit life, and one which has an underlying (one might say 'supernatural') plan."[14]

We call it a "Big Bang," but the beginning of our universe would be better characterized as a highly orchestrated expansion, a "big bloom" as some have called it. From this orchestrated beginning, galaxies, stars, and planets formed, with the planet Earth unusual in its ability to sustain a complex biosphere. These cosmic parameters, and their fine tuning, are also curiously discoverable by us. This too is consistent with the idea that the universe was designed with us in mind.

Given the laws of physics that prevail in our universe, and given an elegant unfolding of those laws and constants from the cosmic beginning, the universe must be as vast as it is and approximately the age that it is to prepare the conditions necessary for a life-friendly solar system and planet Earth. Seen from this perspective, the extra-galactic expanse of our universe, instead of smiting us with smallness, underscores our significance.

All of this we can conclude simply from reading the book of nature. Some three thousand years ago, a poet reached a similar conclusion, reading from that same book of nature but without the benefit of telescopes or physics. "The heavens declare the glory of God,"[15] he wrote. I picture him standing under a night sky, the panoply of stars undimmed by modern daylight pollution. Today we can still experience what he experienced, and even more. Find a patch of earth far from the light pollution of our cities and towns, and step outside on a clear and moonless night. Take in the grandeur of the stars, of the glowing band of the Milky Way. Use a star finder app to pick out the faint but just visible patch of light known as Andromeda, and marvel that you are looking not at a star but at an entire galaxy, a trillion-star cluster of luminescence reaching us from 2.5 million light years away. And this is just one galactic player in a much larger and finely tuned universe.

Physics and the powerful telescopes of our day are not required to experience the sublimity of it all, but they have turned the heavens' insistent whisper of design into something like a triumphant symphony. The discoveries of physics and astronomy have amplified this beautiful symphony. Reason, in turn, urges us to acknowledge that a masterful symphony requires a master composer. What we call intelligent design, the ancients called wisdom, as the psalmist concludes from his examination of nature: "In wisdom you have made them all."[16]

6. THE LIVES OF THE STARS

SOME OF MY FAVORITE OUTDOOR DESTINATIONS ARE HIKES DEEP into the old-growth forests of the Pacific Northwest, their massive trunks the pillars of a cathedral of living green, one stretching out in every direction as far as the eye can see. And of these ancient woods perhaps my favorite is the Hoh Rainforest in Washington's Olympic Peninsula. The ancient trees there feel almost eternal.

Almost.

I remember one testimony to their finitude in particular, an enormous fallen tree, perhaps toppled by the fury of a winter storm. What struck me wasn't that it lay on the ground among standing relatives, but that its rotting trunk had become a veritable nursery of life. All along the top side of the fallen giant sprouted saplings in various stages of new growth. As the wood of the old trunk decayed into a soft, reddish-brown humus that you could easily crumble with one hand, it provided the vital nutrients for the next generation of life. That which had passed away was now the seed bed of what was to come.

This pattern has a circular quality about it, but as a physicist with one foot in cosmology, I know that there is a still older process essential to our living planet that is not circular but linear, and writ not on the canvas of a majestic rainforest but played out on a far larger canvas, that of the cosmos.

You see, all of the life in that rainforest—indeed, all the biological life on earth—requires carbon and other elements that did not even exist when the universe was first born. The atoms that compose the nutrients of life were forged from the blasted remains of stars that shone and perished in long ages past. And for that to happen, our cosmos needs all manner of fine tuning.

Stellar Connections

AS WE study stars, we learn that our lives are inextricably connected with these ancient lights. It may seem that stars are "up there" and we're "down here," but our two realms are not altogether separate. Indeed, one of the great discoveries of modern astronomy is that you and I are made of stardust.

Stars are made up mostly of hydrogen and helium atoms. These two elements, the simplest in the periodic table, formed within the first few minutes of the universe. But in this early period there were no elements beyond hydrogen and helium. If nothing had changed we wouldn't be here, because living things require an array of elements heavier than hydrogen and helium. To understand this, we simply need to know that, with rare exceptions, hydrogen only forms a diatomic molecule with itself (H_2) and helium is a noble gas element that doesn't typically bond to other atoms. On the other extreme, living things require large, complex molecules such as proteins, carbohydrates, and lipids, not to mention DNA, which are built of billions of atoms. Carbon is the key element in all organic molecules, and it was non-existent in the early universe. But thanks to the fusion process in the cores of massive stars, followed by their death throes—a spectacular supernova explosion—our universe acquired carbon and additional heavier elements required for life.

How? Let's take it stage by stage and see.

Gas and Gravity

AS THE matter in the early expanding universe cooled, the attractive force of gravity began to clump together gas clouds of primordial hydrogen and helium. Denser regions within the gas clouds may have initially arisen from quantum fluctuations that grew in magnitude during an early phase of especially rapid expansion known as the inflationary period.[1] As gravity continued to contract the gases together, galaxies and clusters of galaxies eventually formed. Within these nascent galaxies, the clouds of hydrogen and helium gas were further clumped together by gravity to form the first stars.

But how did those denser clumps go from ho-hum clouds of hydrogen and helium to the nuclear fire balls that shine across trillions of miles of space? During the process of gravitational contraction towards a denser center, gas heats up naturally, as gravitational potential energy is converted into heat. We can picture this by imagining the friction encountered by the countless atoms of gas picking up speed as they fall inward toward a common center.

At the same time, as the gas is drawn inward, any original rotation of the gas cloud is amplified by the law of conservation of angular momentum. Ice skaters use this effect when they start a spin with their arms and maybe one leg extended outwards and then bring their limbs inward to increase their rate of rotation.

One additional effect occurs as the gas cloud collapses, for which a master pizza maker serves as an example. When a ball of spinning dough is thrown into the air, it spreads out into a flat disk due to a combination of the effective centrifugal force and the elasticity of the dough. As a star system forms from the collapsing, rotating gas cloud, a similar sort of thing happens. Gravity and effective centrifugal forces work together to flatten the rotating gas cloud into a spinning disk with a hot, dense center. And if it's a star formed later in cosmic history, one like our sun with a helping of heavier metals in the mix, the central region becomes the star, and the surrounding disk constitutes the raw material for the formation of planets.

How to Control an Avalanche

FOR A nebula to collapse and begin the process of star formation, some sort of trigger event is needed. Avalanches on mountain slopes can be triggered by dynamite. To trigger the gravitational collapse of a gaseous nebula, something must first produce denser regions within the nebula. Such events include the collision of one nebula with another, radiation pressure from a nearby hot star, or the powerful blast from the finale of a dying massive star as it undergoes a supernova explosion.

94 / CANCELED SCIENCE /

Spiral galaxies like the Milky Way also show evidence of *spiral density waves* that propagate around the galaxy and help to compress the gas in the spiral arms.[2] Once a denser region of gas starts to draw other material into it, the whole process begins to snowball, or avalanche. The more matter that clumps together, the stronger the gravitational pull, which draws in more matter, which further increases the gravitational pull, and so on.

At this point, one may wonder how the gravitational collapse ever stops once it gets started. Fortunately, the inward crushing force of gravity is eventually matched by an opposing force that creates a balance within the newly forming star. To see how this works, we return to the idea that the gases heat up as they are packed together by gravity. The *ideal gas law* tells us that as the temperature of a gas increases within a given volume, so does its pressure. In a star, it's the outward pressure of the hot, compressed gas core that eventually balances the inward force of gravity.

This is a balancing act, and balance requires feedback. Imagine a mobile with several hanging crosspieces all in balance. You add a little weight to one end of a crosspiece, and it tilts out of balance. To compensate, you'd have to add weight to the other end as well. But there's a limit to this strategy—the string that holds the whole thing up might break. With stars, we find a similar balancing act in which its internal pressure balances the crushing force of gravity. But the whole thing might fail as a star that could support a habitable planet orbiting it, if the ratio of the strength of gravity to the strength of the electromagnetic force were to deviate more than just a little from their actual values.

What does the electromagnetic force have to do with a star's outward pressure? The pressure needed to balance gravity also has to match the conditions necessary to achieve nuclear fusion in the star's core, which in turn depends upon the electrical repulsion between nuclei. This means that if the universal electromagnetic strength were somehow different from what it is, so too would be the outward pressure for a given star. And although gravity can provide a crushing force, it needs a huge amount of mass to become very strong. As a force of nature, gravity is the ultimate weakling. Astrophysicists have calculated that the extreme weakness of gravity compared to the electromagnetic force (to the tune of about a trillion times a trillion times a trillion (10^{36}) times weaker) is necessary for the gravity-pressure balancing act to make a star like our sun shine and support life on a planet like Earth.[3] To get a stable stellar balance at all requires fine tuning the ratio of the strengths of these forces to one part in 10^{35}.

The Stellar Furnace: Matter into Energy

TO REPLENISH the energy a star radiates into space, the laws of nature congenially provide an energy source to keep the star's core hot. When gas is compressed sufficiently, its temperature and density reach a threshold where nuclear fusion ignites and releases energy.

To understand this, we need just a little nuclear physics. I'll make it quick and painless, leaving out a lot of the details.

All atoms heavier than hydrogen contain a nucleus composed of a combination of protons and neutrons. (The nucleus of a hydrogen atom is just a single lonely proton.) Protons and neutrons are tightly bound together in the nucleus by one of the four fundamental forces of nature, the strong nuclear force. Since the protons in the nucleus each have a positive charge, they fiercely resist being packed together. If it weren't for the fact that the strong nuclear force can overcome the electrical repulsion of the protons, the only element in the universe would be hydrogen with its solitary proton nucleus. In such a universe, we wouldn't exist.

The strong nuclear force is, as the name suggests, strong. But its range is very short. The protons or neutrons essentially have to be touching before the strong nuclear force can bind them together. Because of their electrical repulsion, the only way to get the protons close enough together for this to happen is if they are moving very fast and happen to fly towards one another on a collision course. Then their momentum can carry them together against their mutual repulsion. Once they almost touch, the strong nuclear force acts like nuclear Velcro and binds them together in the process known as nuclear fusion.

As is often the case, the story gets more interesting with a closer look. The range of the strong nuclear force is so short (about one quadrillionth of a meter) that the repulsive force between the positive charges of the protons makes it almost impossible for them to get close enough to fuse at the sun's core temperature. And yet fusion does occur there. A remarkable work-around exists involving the quantum mechanical wave function of the proton, in which its essence is extended several hundred times farther than it would be otherwise. This allows the life-giving fusion process to occur in the sun. Without the quantum wave function extending the proton's reach, the sun's temperature would have to be more than a hundred times hotter to be able to produce energy by fusion. Our sun's mass is much too small for gravity to produce enough compression to make its core that hot, so no fusion would occur without the additional quantum effects. Sunshine is thus an amazing thing, and without this coordination of several properties of nature, the sun wouldn't shine and we wouldn't be here.

To start the fusion process that keeps the sun shining, the nuclei deep inside the sun have to get moving very fast. In the core of a star, a natural mechanism exists by which the nuclei (starting with single-proton hydrogen nuclei) can be made to move fast enough to allow fusion to occur. As gravity compresses the star's core material, it heats up, and when a gas becomes hotter, the particles of the gas move faster and faster.

Not only do the nuclei have to be moving fast, there has to be a high enough density of them so that collisions between them can occur. At a temperature of about ten million degrees kelvin, the force of gravity has packed together sufficiently many fast-moving protons in the core of a star like our sun so that a self-sustaining fusion reaction can begin. The initial fusion process converts four hydrogen nuclei into one helium nucleus. The energy released in the fusion process replenishes the star's heat lost by radiation into space. The fusion furnace in a star's core provides the heat needed to maintain the star's internal pressure, keeping the relentless force of gravity at bay.

Where does all this fresh energy come from? A small amount of matter is transformed into energy when the four protons that go into the fusion reaction convert into one helium nucleus.

But it gets even stranger. Two of the original four protons transform during fusion into neutrons, releasing two particles of antimatter in the process. The proton-to-neutron transformation is governed by the weak force, another one of the four fundamental forces of nature. Thanks to the weak force, the rate of nuclear fusion is kept at a level that allows the sun to produce the right amount of energy for a sufficiently long period of time to sustain life on Earth. As one physics site bluntly puts it, "Without the weak force, the sun would cease to exist."[4]

The antimatter particles that result from the action of the weak force are called positrons, or antielectrons. After being emitted, their lives are short as they quickly meet up with normal electrons in the core of the star. These particle-antiparticle pairs quickly annihilate each other, converting their masses into a burst of energy.

How does it feel to know that part the warmth of sunshine we feel on Earth comes from matter-antimatter annihilation in the core of the sun?

When we hear how nuclear fusion creates energy, it sounds almost like science fiction. Fusion releases heat by converting matter to energy, part of which comes from a matter-antimatter throwdown. But of course it's not science fiction. It's reality as described in part by Einstein's famous equation, $E=mc^2$.

By calculating the total amount of energy the sun emits, we can work backwards and calculate how much matter is converted to energy in the core of the sun. The amount is prodigious—almost five million tons per second! That's equal to about five hundred trainloads of gravel, with each train made up of one hundred cars fully loaded. This huge amount of mass disappears every second from our sun due to nuclear fusion, and the output is pure energy.

Every second throughout its adult existence, the sun has converted about five million tons of mass directly into energy and radiated it into space. You might wonder that the sun hasn't completely consumed itself at this rate. The reason is simply that the sun is really, really big. Its mass is about 333,000 times that of planet Earth. The sun is so massive that over its projected ten-billion-year lifespan, only about 0.07% of its mass will get converted to energy.

Seeing the Unseen

How CAN scientists know that the nuclear fusion process just described actually takes place in the core of the sun? We cannot observe the sun's core, not even close. It lies some 700,000 km below the sun's surface, a distance almost twice as far as from the Earth to the moon.

To discern what conditions are like deep down in the center of the sun, astronomers use computer models based on the known laws of physics, and then see if the conclusions match up with other lines of evidence. Such computations suggest that the central density of the sun is about fifteen times denser than lead, and yet it's still a gas! This can only happen because the sun's central temperature is also so high, about fifteen million kelvin.[5]

What other lines of evidence might confirm this picture of the sun's core? There are many we won't go into here. I'll mention just one, a new way of "seeing" directly inside the sun. It doesn't involve light. It involves a byproduct of fusion.

Each time a hydrogen-to-helium fusion reaction takes place in a star's core, two subatomic particles called *neutrinos* are emitted. These little neutral particles stream constantly out of the sun and fly off through space at nearly the speed of light. Countless billions of them hit the Earth every second, and most of them pass right through the entire Earth as if it were simply transparent. However, scientists have succeeded in building neutrino detectors, which confirm that the expected number of neutrinos from the sun is in fact being produced. This evidence validates the nuclear model for the sun's energy production process.[6]

An Aging Star

WHEN I described how much mass the sun converts to energy every day, and how even over billions of years this barely puts a dent in the total mass of the sun, it would be easy to get the impression that sun-like stars are, for all practical purposes, unchanging. Fortunately for us, they do change.

We have already touched on the early phase of a star's life. All stars begin their lives in a nursery of hydrogen and helium gas clouds. To produce energy from these raw materials, gravity needs to collapse an interstellar gas cloud into a giant sphere, increasing its density and temperature in the process. Once the central temperature and density reach critical thresholds, the fusion of hydrogen into helium begins, and a star is born.

As long as hydrogen fuel remains in the core of the star, the star shines in what astronomers call the "main sequence" phase of its life. This prime-of-life phase covers about 90% of a star's overall life. The lifespan of a given star depends upon how fast it burns its fuel and how much fuel it has to start with. The rate at which a star burns its fuel is proportional to its mass. The more massive a star is, the more heat and pressure it needs in order to withstand the greater gravitational force of compression.

Of course, a more massive star also has more mass to burn. But the physics works out such that the more massive a star is, the faster it runs out of gas, resulting in lifespans that vary dramatically with mass. The main sequence lifespan of a very massive star with forty times the mass of the sun would only be one million years. In contrast, the lifespan of a small star of half the sun's mass would stretch to 56 billion years— that's over four times the present age of the universe![7] Based on this, we conclude that no small stars have yet burned out in the history of the universe.

Some people have complained that if the universe was designed with humans as the centerpiece, then why would it be so old? One answer could be that it's a matter of perspective: from the point of view of humans, the universe is extremely old, but from the point of view of the most common stars, the universe is really quite young. Most small stars have barely entered adolescence in their lifespans since the beginning of the universe.

Let's take a closer look at what happens as a star ages. Most of the action is in the core of the star, the nuclear furnace that keeps the star alive. This central region is the only place hot enough and dense enough to sustain a hydrogen fusion reaction. The entire star contains hydrogen, but after its core runs out of hydrogen, its primary fuel tank is empty. At this stage, about 90% of the star's life is over.

In the final 10% of its life, a star of at least the sun's mass undergoes an impressive finale as it ages towards its demise. First, the star's core begins to contract, due to its dwindling nuclear energy output. The core of the star is by this time a sphere of compressed helium gas, the byproduct of its hydrogen fusion stage.

Helium can also serve as a nuclear fusion fuel, but it requires a much higher temperature than hydrogen—about one hundred million kelvin. As gravity compresses the star's core, it heats up until a spherical shell of hydrogen gas surrounding the helium core begins to fuse. This extra fusion energy generates enough outward pressure to cause the outer region (or "envelope") of the star to swell up to 30–100 times its original size.[8] The star then becomes what is known as a "red giant." Its reddish color comes from its cooler surface temperature—a result of the expansion of the gas of the outer layers.

Except in the smallest stars, the gravitational compression of the core can eventually raise the temperature enough so that helium fusion begins, which releases even more energy. The helium in a star's core is the very same type of gas you might find in a grocery store to fill balloons for a party. The sun produces it continuously from the fusion of hydrogen. You might even say that the sun is preparing to throw a party! Did you know that helium was unknown on Earth until it was first discovered in the sun? Scientists first found evidence for helium when making careful observations of the wavelengths of light seen in the solar spectrum. The name "helium" was then coined from the Greek word-root for the sun.

That's some impressive detective work, but here's the key point: The detectives wouldn't have been around to detect anything if not for something remarkable about this multi-phase fusion process in the life of all but the smallest stars. The process eventually creates carbon, and does so thanks to a particularly striking example of fine tuning.

Forming Carbon, the Atom of Life

CARBON IS an essential element for all life as we know it. Science fiction movies may present alien creatures based on silicone or some other element, but astrobiologists see carbon and water (made of hydrogen and oxygen) as indispensable ingredients for any physical life in the universe, and certainly for any such advanced life. This is because carbon and water have crucial capacities not possessed by any other element or compound. However, if the nuclear force had been slightly different from what it is, the universe would have been devoid of carbon. Carbon fuses from helium in stellar cores by a remarkable process. Three helium nuclei have to randomly collide almost simultaneously to fuse into a single carbon nucleus. This unlikely conjunction is needed because the simpler merging of just two helium nuclei results in an isotope of beryllium that is extremely unstable.

Under normal conditions, the beryllium isotope would fall apart before a third helium could combine with it to form carbon. This would have short-circuited the formation of carbon and other heavier elements via the fusion process. It would also short-circuit the possibility that life could ever exist.

But since carbon exists in relatively high abundance in the universe, astronomer Fred Hoyle suspected that some "coincidental" circumstances must allow it to exist. He predicted a unique resonance of nuclear energies that would increase the chances of carbon forming by the fusion of three helium nuclei. The nuclear resonance sought by Hoyle is an excited state of carbon that would have an energy commensurate with the total energy the fast-moving beryllium and helium nuclei would have as they collided. With the excited state resonance, the newly formed carbon nucleus can safely shed the extra energy in the form of a gamma ray photon, rather than falling apart from the energy of its formation. Hoyle's predicted resonance of the carbon nucleus was found at the required energy value to allow carbon to be formed in sufficient quantities in the cores of stars.

Is this an example of fine tuning of the parameters of nature? Hoyle, despite a reputation for religious skepticism, was so impressed with how this worked that he wrote, "I do not believe that any scientist who examined the evidence would fail to draw the inference that the laws of nuclear physics have been deliberately designed with regard to the consequences they produce inside the stars."[9]

Stephen Hawking, in his book *The Grand Design*, airily dismisses this and multiple other discoveries of fine tuning with an appeal to the multiverse theory.[10] We discussed in the previous chapter the problems with that explanation for fine tuning. But in a nutshell, recall that the multiverse is the idea that there are gazillions of other universes—undetected and undetectable—each with differently configured laws and constants, and we shouldn't be surprised that we live in one of the lucky universes with a life-friendly configuration since, otherwise, we wouldn't be here to notice our good fortune.

Such a desperate appeal is testimony to the strength of the fine-tuning evidence of design. If that evidence could be dismissed by a more straightforward appeal to naturalistic processes within our universe, scientists would hardly bother appealing to the genie of a universe-generating multiverse machine and its countless offspring, forever beyond detection or measurement.

Final Stages: Low-Mass Stars

As WE continue our story of the life cycles of stars, we need to distinguish stars by their mass. The mass of a star determines its final stage of stellar burning. Stars up to about eight times as massive as our sun are called "low mass" stars. (Yes, our sun is huge compared to planet earth, but it's a lightweight compared to some stars.) These low-mass stars lack the gravitational weight necessary to contract and heat their cores sufficiently to continue to fuse heavier elements past the formation of carbon and oxygen (and possibly silicon).

Each heavier element requires a higher temperature to initiate the next fusion cycle. The reason: Heavier elements have more positively charged protons that must be forced together at each fusion step. More protons means more positive charge, and more positive charge means more repulsive force between the nuclei. That greater repulsive force has to be overcome for fusion to occur. The nuclei can get pushed past the repulsive force and fuse only if they are moving fast enough, and this only happens when they are at a high enough temperature.

As a predominantly carbon core forms within a low mass star, the star's outer layers expand to the point where it loses gravitational control over them. Aided by radiation pressure, the star bellows its outer layers into space. These hot, expanding gases form a transient, glowing display known as a planetary nebula. (See Figure 6.1.) This name is a misleading leftover from earlier days in astronomy when it was thought that these glowing smoke rings around stars had something to do with the formation of planets. Now, however, we know that they represent the last gasp of a dying star. Even this dying breath, however, contributes to life. The

Figure 6.1. The Helix nebula, the last gasp of a dying star.

gases expelled into space by a dying star include a significant amount of carbon, essential for life.[11]

As the gases of the star's outer layer disperse into space, the hot inner core of the star becomes exposed for the first time in its long history. This predominantly carbon core is like a cinder pulled from a fire; it's still very hot, but it hasn't any more fuel to burn. Gravity wins the upper hand with the core and compresses it into a remarkably dense state known as *degenerate matter*. This term stems from quantum mechanics, and refers to the state of the electrons in the dense stellar core. The wave-like aspects of the electrons resist packing together any tighter than quantum properties will allow, but those limits still allow things to get unusually dense. In fact, the density of this burnt-out star is so great that a sugar-cube sized bit of it would weigh about two tons on Earth.[12]

These stellar cores are called white dwarfs, referring to their white-hot temperatures and small size. A typical white dwarf is about Earth-sized (a million times smaller than the volume of the sun), but its mass is still comparable to the sun's mass (about 330,000 times the mass of the Earth). White dwarfs are composed mainly of carbon (and some oxygen) in a highly compressed state. This has led some astronomers to compare them to giant crystals or diamonds in space—and galaxies are strewn with these jewels.[13] Since their fusion days are behind them, as they radiate their heat into space they simply cool down and grow dimmer with time.

That's what happens if the white dwarf is by itself. But if it has a companion white dwarf, the end game is dramatically different.

Exploding White Dwarfs

OVER 50% of all stars in our galaxy are not solitary stars but are composed of binary pairs. Binary stars are composed of two stars orbiting each other. If a white dwarf forms as one of a binary pair, it has a way to briefly resuscitate itself. It does this by stealing gas from the outer layers of its companion star. This can happen if they orbit closely enough, especially if the companion star has expanded into its red giant phase.

As the stolen gas builds up on the surface of the white dwarf, it is compressed and heated by the white dwarf's tremendous surface gravity. Eventually, the surface gas buildup (which is composed of the usual hydrogen-helium mix) becomes dense and hot enough so that it suddenly fuses. The released thermonuclear energy then blows these hot surface gases out into space, producing an incandescent display.

The expanding shell of superheated gas emits energy at a rate far greater than the little white dwarf would normally emit, so its brightness suddenly increases by up to a million times. It can then appear to observers on Earth that a new star (a "nova") has suddenly appeared, since the original white dwarf may have been too dim to be visible. This flare-up is temporary, however, and over a few weeks it fades again from view. As time goes on, the expanding gases simply cool and dissipate into space. But later, the whole process may happen again as more gas transfers between the two stars, since the surface fusion explosion of built-up gas doesn't have enough energy to destroy either star.[14]

Since white dwarfs are composed of degenerate matter, they have some unusual properties. One of these is that the more massive a white dwarf becomes, the *smaller* it grows. This leads to an upper mass limit on the mass of a white dwarf, known as the Chandrasekhar limit, beyond which the white dwarf becomes unstable against gravitational collapse and rapidly morphs into something else. This mass limit is 1.4 times the mass of our sun. Suppose a white dwarf in a binary system steals enough mass from its companion star so that its mass reaches the Chandrasekhar limit. Due to its small size and large mass, gravity will then implode the white dwarf in on itself. This suddenly increases its internal pressure and temperature, and ignites the entire star in a massive carbon fusion explosion known as a supernova.

The runaway fusion process in the collapsed white dwarf effectively fuses its entire mass into a mix of heavier elements that are blown into interstellar space by the explosion. Many elements essential to our planet and to living things are formed and dispersed through interstellar space

106 / Canceled Science /

during these supernova explosions. This includes essential elements such as silicon, calcium, iron, and nickel.[15]

This type of exploding white dwarf is termed a Type Ia supernova. The energy it releases during the explosion rivals the energy output of an entire galaxy. Can you imagine one supernova shining as brightly as the combined light of a hundred billion stars! These Type Ia supernovae also have the unique property that every one releases nearly the same amount of energy as all the others. This happens because the supernova chain reaction begins when each one, steadily sucking mass from its companion star, reaches 1.4 times the mass of the sun.

Astronomers have capitalized on this property of uniform brightness by using Type Ia supernovae as "standard candles." Wherever a standard candle is seen, its absolute brightness is known even if it appears dimmer due to being a great distance away. The apparent brightness of a star decreases as the square of its distance from Earth. Knowing this relationship allows astronomers to calculate the distance to any galaxy in which they observe a Type Ia supernova. This technique gives our most accurate estimates of the distances to faraway galaxies. As discussed in a previous chapter, knowledge of galactic distances, coupled with measurements of their recessional velocities, has provided us valuable information on the expansion rate and age of the universe.

Massive Stars—Grand Finales

Our survey of stellar life cycles isn't finished yet. We still need to consider the fate of high mass stars—those with more than eight times the mass of our sun. After these stars consume the hydrogen in their cores, they will also transition into the red giant phase. The difference is that the great mass of these stars provide enough gravitational compression to heat their cores enough to carry the fusion process beyond carbon and oxygen. Carbon begins to fuse at about 600 million kelvin, forming elements such as neon and magnesium. Oxygen requires a temperature of over one billion kelvin to begin to fuse into sulfur, silicon, and phosphorus.[16]

As soon as one phase of fusion fuel is depleted, the star's core pressure wanes. Gravity then compresses the core and further heats it until the next phase of fusion ignites. This process can result in several layers undergoing the fusion of different elements at the same time in the core of a massive star. Heavier elements will fuse deeper into the core where it's hottest, and the lighter elements will fuse farther out. The fusion process continues nicely until the stage at which silicon fuses into iron. Iron is a unique element in that it is the stopping point for a star's ability to produce energy from fusion. It's impossible to get any energy out of iron or heavier elements by the fusion process, so when iron begins to build up in the star's core, its fusion fuel tank is nearly empty.

When a car runs out of gas, it simply comes to a stop, but when a massive star runs out of fuel, it explodes! Here's how the process works. When the last bit of silicon fuses into iron, the star can no longer produce heat in its core to maintain sufficient pressure to withstand the crushing force of gravity. The result is an epic implosion of the iron core, which collapses from Earth-sized to city-sized in less than half a second.[17]

It may seem strange that a ball of iron could be compressed to a smaller size, but under the extreme pressure and heat in the core of the massive star, the nature of matter begins to transform. The electrons and the protons of the core material combine into neutrons. These neutrons can be packed very tightly together since they lack electrical charge and do not repel each other. So the volume of the star's core drops by a factor of more than ten million. With the core suddenly imploded, the rest of the star acts like a skyscraper with its foundation blown away, and the whole thing begins to fall inward.

But only so much material can be packed into the central region, and the collapsing core soon rebounds, sending a shock wave outward through the star. The outward pressure of the shock wave is aided by a flood of neutrinos released by the combining protons and electrons. The resulting outflow of energy blasts all but the innermost core of the doomed star into surrounding space. Astronomers call this event a Type II supernova. The superheated, rapidly expanding ball of gas releases a vast amount of energy across the electromagnetic spectrum and in the outpouring flood of neutrinos.

The fundamental physics of the core-collapse supernova mechanism is understood, but detailed computational simulations have proved intensely difficult. Using some of the most powerful computational tools available, researchers have found that the dynamical physics in the core collapse and rebounding shock wave must involve a complex balance of variables in order to actually sustain a supernova explosion.[18] When you think about it, a supernova explosion is paradoxical: the trigger event for the explosion is an implosion. The challenge in modeling a supernova theoretically is finding a mechanism to transform the rapidly collapsing core of a massive star into a violent outward explosion. The rebounding shock wave mentioned earlier, when modeled computationally, needed some extra "oomph" to blast the outer layers of the star into space. Help came from another source that, again, seems paradoxical—neutrinos.

Remember, neutrinos are the ghost particles that can pass clear through the solid Earth without touching anything. You wouldn't think that ghost particles could lend a shoulder to heft the outer layers of the star out into space, and in normal quantities, you're right. But the core collapse process produces such phenomenal quantities of neutrinos in a fraction of a second that their combined effect does the job.

How many neutrinos are we talking about? A lot. The Earth-sized iron core of a large star has about as much mass as our sun, meaning it has over 10^{56} protons, each of which gets converted into a neutron and a neutrino as the core collapses into an ultra-dense ball of neutrons. This hoard of neutrinos forms an improbable snowplow and assists the shock wave in successfully blowing the star apart.[19]

In nature, these mighty explosions occurred sufficiently often in the earlier history of our galaxy to seed interstellar space with the vital concentrations of heavy elements necessary to form a life-sustaining planet. Evidence for the gradual buildup of heavy elements due to supernovae is found by measuring the composition of elements in stars that formed at different stages in the history of our galaxy. Astronomers have found that young stars show a concentration of heavy elements that is 20–30 times higher than that of very old stars.[20]

Sharing the Wealth

IF SPECTACULAR supernova explosions never occurred, all of the useful elements produced by stellar fusion would forever be locked up deep within stars. In addition, all of the elements heavier than iron (up to uranium, number 92) are not produced in nature during a star's main sequence life span, since their formation only proceeds by reactions that consume energy rather than producing it. A supernova explosion, however, provides a vast amount of extra energy that could result in the formation of heavier elements.

Remarkably, it's possible to obtain evidence supporting this theory of ancient nucleosynthesis. Since the elements heavier than iron are thought to be only produced in the transient supernova phase, we would expect that these elements are less abundant in our universe than the lighter elements, and such proves to be the case.[21] Such confirmed predictions help scientists have confidence in their theories. Further corroboration comes from confirmation of the prediction that the even-numbered elements (those with an even number of protons) will be more abundant than the odd-numbered elements. This prediction also matches observational evidence, as the graph in Figure 6.2 shows for measurements from our solar system. The reason for it is that fusion within the cores of stars most easily proceeds by adding a helium nucleus onto an already existing nucleus. The helium nucleus, composed of two protons and two neutrons, is like a brick in the process of element construction.[22]

Throughout the history of a galaxy, supernovae serve to enrich the interstellar medium with the full array of elements needed for life. The preponderance of material in nebulae is still made up of just hydrogen and helium, but over time, about 2% of the total mix is built up to consist of elements heavier than helium. This enriched content of interstellar gases contains the right mixture to form not only a star like our sun, but also the variety of planets in our solar system. The heavier elements

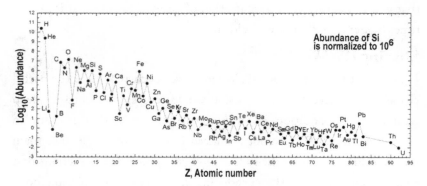

Figure 6.2. Abundance of the chemical elements in the Solar System.

produced in supernovae allow for the formation of planets with solid surfaces, like our Earth.

A Delicate Balance

ALTHOUGH SUPERNOVAE serve a vital role in manufacturing life-essential elements, as discussed previously they also pose a serious danger to life. A supernova explosion releases prodigious amounts of radiation that could sterilize any planet orbiting around a nearby star system. So it's crucial for us that the rate of supernovae in our galaxy has diminished throughout eons of time to a low level today. In fact, the rate is so low that only five have been close enough to be observed with the naked eye since AD 1,000.

Supernovae also play a role in determining where in the galaxy the conditions are best for a planet like Earth. Near the galactic center the density of stars in space is much higher than it is in our location (our sun is about two-thirds of the way to the edge from the center of the galaxy). The higher density of stars near the central region of the galaxy would increase the probability of sterilization events from supernova explosions. More crowded star conditions would also increase the risk of a near-collision accident (like driving in rush hour in Los Angeles compared to driving along a country road in rural Indiana). Gravitational encounters with other stars could disrupt our solar system's planetary orbits.

On the other hand, too far from the galactic center the initial frequency of supernovae would have been too low to sufficiently enrich the interstellar medium with life-essential heavy elements. It turns out that our solar system resides within a narrow band circling about 26,000 light years from the galactic core, known to astronomers as the "Galactic Habitable Zone."[23] Here there are enough heavy elements for planetary formation, but it's not so crowded as to be in great danger of other stars gravitationally disrupting our planetary orbits, or nearby supernovae explosions, or too much radiation from the higher density of stars near the galactic center. Earth's location within our galaxy's habitable zone is ideal for allowing the long-term existence of life on our planet.

Even more impressive, the ideal zone for habitability coincides with an ideal location for making astronomical discoveries about our cosmos. Our solar system's location within the Milky Way's disk region, in between two spiral arms, means that the "light pollution" from other stars and nebulae is not as great as it would be in regions more densely populated by stars. The combined light from more crowded galactic regions such as spiral arms or the central nuclear bulge would dim our view of the universe and limit our ability to discover information about the distant universe and its history. This is another of many instances where the parameters for habitability coincide with the parameters well suited to make scientific discoveries—not the sort of happy convergence one would expect to find in a universe that was habitable due only to blind chance.[24]

Neutron Stars: Galactic Lighthouses

Now, let's consider what's left behind after a massive star explodes as a supernova. Unlike the supernovae resulting from white dwarfs that exceed their mass limit, supernovae from massive stars produce an ultra-compact core object. The implosion of the iron core of a massive star results in a solid sphere of neutrons packed together so tightly that it resembles a giant nucleus in space. Although enormous compared to any atomic nucleus, the neutron star, as it's called, is ridiculously small compared to any normal star. The diameter of a neutron star is only about twelve miles across, less than the length of Manhattan island. That's compared to a diameter of about 865,000 miles for our sun.[25] A neutron star's mass, however, can be up to about twice the mass of our sun.[26] The force of gravity at the neutron star's surface is so powerful that it compresses the neutrons into an unbelievably dense state. Drop a sugar-cube sized lump of neutron star into your coffee cup, and good luck lifting the cup. The little cube would have a mass of about one hundred million tons—the same as almost a cubic kilometer of rock.[27]

It's an amazing testimony to the transparency of nature that physicists could predict the bizarre properties of neutron stars more than thirty years before anyone ever detected their existence. When they finally were discovered, it was by accident and not because a search for them was underway. In 1967, a graduate student from England named Jocelyn Bell, using a simple radio telescope, detected a signal composed of periodic, rapidly varying pulses. This might seem unremarkable, but no natural source then known could produce such a signal coming from space. To understand why, we consider an astronomical rule of thumb regarding how quickly a star can change its intensity. The laws of physics require that the pulse duration can't be any shorter than the time it takes for light to travel across the star's radius. For example, the sun, with its radius of 700,000 km, cannot noticeably vary in intensity on a time scale shorter than about 2.3 seconds (given by dividing the sun's radius by the speed of light, which is 300,000 km/sec).

The smallest stars known in 1967 were Earth-sized white dwarfs, but they would still be more than forty times too big to emit the short pulses detected by Jocelyn Bell.[28] As the story goes, the unknown source of these pulses was initially called "LGM," for little green men. However, as we discuss in Chapter 9, an intelligently originated message would not simply be a repetitious signal, for such a signal could not contain significant information. Therefore, the pulses were deemed natural in origin.

Could the source be an ultra-compact, spinning neutron star, predicted over thirty years earlier? With their small radii (more than 600 times smaller than white dwarfs), neutron stars could theoretically emit the rapidly varying pulsed signals that had been detected. Still, the mechanism for generating such pulses remained a question. Fortunately, the physics behind the formation and properties of a neutron star provided the answer. Remember that a neutron star forms when the core of a massive star implodes. Normal stars rotate rather sedately (our sun rotates on its own axis about once every four weeks). But as the core of a star collapses inward, the rate of rotation increases—an effect caused by the conservation of angular momentum. In this way, a neutron star could end up rotating faster than once per second.

The implosion also endows the star with an ultra-strong magnetic field, up to a quadrillion times stronger than Earth's.[29]

With its fast rotation rate and ultra-strong magnetic field, a neutron star generates powerful "lighthouse" beams of radiation along the axis of its magnetic field. These beams rapidly sweep across space in an ever-circling arc as the star rotates. If the Earth happens to lie in the path of one of these beams, a sharp pulse of radiation is received with each rotation of the star. The repeating pulses have earned neutron stars detected in this manner the name "pulsars." A famous pulsar lies within the Crab Nebula, which is the remnant of a supernova seen on Earth in the year 1054 (it was so bright that it could be seen in the daytime). The Crab Nebula pulsar spins at about thirty revolutions per second. Imagine something more massive than our sun rotating thirty times per second! That's about twice as fast as the wheels on your car rotate when driving at freeway speeds.

Confirming General Relativity

Pulsars are fascinating in their own right, but they've also given scientists an opportunity to test and confirm several aspects of theoretical physics, including Einstein's theory of general relativity. Einstein predicted that a rapidly changing distribution of matter should emanate gravity waves that travel through space. Until recently, however, the direct detection of such waves eluded the best efforts of scientists, since the force of gravity is so weak compared to the other forces of nature. Indirect detection of gravity waves occurred in 1974, when a binary pulsar was discovered with two pulsars orbiting each other rapidly—their orbital period was just 7.75 hours.[30] Such rapid motion of these massive compact objects would send out gravitational radiation, if the predictions of general relativity were correct. The energy carried away by the gravity waves should cause the orbital period to gradually shorten as the pulsars slowly spiral closer together. Astronomers observed this effect, thereby providing indirect confirmation of the theoretical predictions of gravitational waves. The discoverers of this phenomenon, Joseph Taylor and Russell Hulse, received the 1993 Nobel Prize in physics for their work.

Another property of pulsars that has allowed physicists to confirm predictions has to do with their rotation rate. We detect pulsars via their powerful lighthouse beams of radiation, emitted along their magnetic axes as they rotate. But where does the energy for those beams come from? A neutron star doesn't produce energy like a normal star does. The main source of energy for the lighthouse beams comes from the rotational energy of the dense star. Estimating the amount of energy emitted within the beams, and knowing the relation between rotation rate and rotational energy, allows scientists to predict the rate at which a pulsar's spin should slow. The frequency of the pulses can be accurately measured and from this it has been shown that the spin rate does indeed slow with time, confirming the physical model of pulsars as spinning lighthouses. As encouraging as these results were in confirming scientific understanding of exotic events in the universe, more discoveries were coming.

Catching a Gravity Wave

The first direct detection of gravitational waves occurred on September 14, 2015, by the dual advanced LIGO (Laser Interferometer Gravitational-Wave Observatory) instruments, located in Louisiana and Washington state.[31] Analysis of the signals matched the predictions of the inward spiraling and merging of two massive black holes, rapidly orbiting each other in a distant galaxy. This momentous detection was the culmination of one hundred years of prediction, speculation, and searching for gravitational waves, which began with Einstein's solutions of his general relativity equations in 1916, indicating that such waves should exist. The advanced LIGO facility began its first observing run in September 2015, and just days after it became fully operational the gravitational wave signal arrived at Earth, after having travelled at the speed of light for the last 1.3 billion years from a distant galaxy.

The timing of these events is truly remarkable. Since the detected signal is transient—lasting less than half a second—if the LIGO detectors had been delayed by just a couple of weeks in starting their initial operation, the signal would have passed by unnoticed. A gravitational wave is something like a seismic wave propagating through space. It's a shaking of the space-time fabric of the heavens. The strength of the signal detected in 2015 was extremely small, since its source was in a distant galaxy, but if the source had been within ten light years of Earth, we probably could have felt it. That's how strong the wave was at its source.

Other gravitational waves have been detected since then. A second confirmed wave was detected on December 26, 2015, and there are certainly many more to come, initiating a new era of gravitational-wave astronomy.

Point of No Return

The upper mass limit of a neutron star is set by the constraints of quantum mechanics and general relativity theory. These theories indicate that if a neutron star's mass exceeds a certain limit, it will eventually morph into something even stranger than a neutron star. In the overall progression of matter through the life cycle of a large-mass star, it moves from a diffuse interstellar nebula, to a star with a core of increasing density, to a neutron star. But one more cataclysmic transformation awaits it, another collapse such that its density becomes so great that it forms a black hole.

Whenever I ask an astronomy class what topics they would most like to learn about during the course, black holes come out on the top of the list. The popular conception of a black hole—a hole in space out of which there is no return—can be fascinating to think about. Black holes are an inevitable result of too much matter being packed into too small a space. When this happens, the surface gravity of the object becomes so strong that the only way to escape would be to travel faster than the speed of light, a speed limit that cannot be exceeded.

Any planet or star has a certain "escape velocity," specifying how fast something has to move to escape its gravitational pull and never fall back. For the planet Earth, the escape velocity is about seven miles per second. This is the speed the Apollo astronauts had to attain in order to break away from Earth's orbit on their journey to the moon.

The more mass a planet or star has within a given radius, the higher its escape velocity. The escape velocity from the surface of a neutron star can be more than half the speed of light. How could it get any higher? If the ball of neutrons that forms from the collapsing core of a massive star is more than about twice the mass of our sun, gravity becomes so strong that the neutron sphere cannot withstand its crushing force. It then implodes into an even smaller volume, pushing the escape velocity of the object past the speed of light and forming a black hole.

As we saw earlier, according to general relativity theory, matter can and does bend space. As matter collapses into a black hole, its density becomes so great that it bends space more and more sharply. Any matter that falls into a black hole may be crushed to an ultra-ultra dense material at the center, but we don't have the physics to accurately describe its properties.

At a certain distance out from the center of the black hole, relativity theory applies, and it predicts a boundary known as *the event horizon.* The event horizon is the point of no return for anything approaching a black hole—nothing that goes in can ever come back out, not even light. (The theoretical prediction of "Hawking radiation" suggests that black holes can eventually evaporate by losing a tiny amount of their gravitational potential energy every time they capture one of a pair of virtual particles that come into existence near the event horizon. For stellar-mass black holes, the rate of evaporation is extremely slow, taking many times the age of the universe to make such a black hole disappear.[32]) The escape velocity at the event horizon is equal to the speed of light. This horizon around the center of the black hole forms at a radius proportional to the amount of mass inside. For a black hole with a mass equal to the mass of the sun, the event horizon would be at a radius of about three kilometers. Black holes are quite strange in that a normal hole can be filled in by putting material into it, but if you try that with a black hole it just gets bigger.

Monster Black Holes

Compelling evidence from astronomy points to the existence of supermassive black holes at the centers of most galaxies.[33] The center of our own Milky Way Galaxy has a black hole with a mass of about 4.3 million times the mass of our sun. Evidence for this is shown by radio telescope observations of the tight orbits of multiple stars around the center point,[34] observational work that earned Reinhard Benzel and Andrea Ghez a share of the 2020 Nobel Prize in Physics. The radius of such a massive black hole would still only be about eight million miles. If it were placed in the center of our solar system, its event horizon would be less than a fourth of the way out to the orbit of our innermost planet, Mercury. However, its gravity would be so strong that Earth would have to orbit about two thousand times faster just to keep from being sucked in. Any mass that gets sucked into a black hole falls faster than the speed of light (yes, this is possible in a situation like this, where you're talking about matter moving with the flow of space itself) into the very center. The center of a black hole is called a "singularity"—a mathematical term for something that becomes infinite—in this case the density of matter. Gravity is believed to crush all the matter that falls into a black hole into a single point (perhaps only slightly spread out due to quantum effects). A theory of quantum gravity would be needed to fully describe these extreme conditions, and scientists are still searching for a successful theory of this type.

Supermassive black holes may have formed along with their galaxies as matter was falling together under the influence of gravity. Once a black hole forms in the crowded stellar region in the center of a galaxy, it may absorb, or *eat*, other material, including gases and whole stars. As material falls toward a black hole it swirls around like water going down a drain, forming an accretion disk. The rapidly swirling material in the disk heats up due to friction and emits a messy spectrum of intense radiation, including dangerous x-rays.[35]

Early in the history of a galaxy, the average rate that material fell into its central black hole was greater than in its later history. This resulted in ultra-powerful emissions of radiation from the accretion disk around the black hole. The radiation from the center of young galaxies can be hundreds to even thousands of times more intense than the combined energy from all the stars in our galaxy.[36] Such objects are called quasars. They are primarily detected only at great distances from the Earth, meaning that they were mostly active earlier in the history of the universe. Remember that due to the finite speed of light through space, the farther out we look from Earth, the further back into the past we see. Nature's time machine allows astronomers to view the universe at virtually any time in the past, almost back to the beginning of time. This illustrates a property of the universe that has been labeled "discoverability." Not only does our universe exhibit fine tuning for habitability, but as touched on above, some of the same conditions that allow life to flourish on Earth also allow humans to discover knowledge about the universe that would otherwise be inaccessible.[37]

Falling into a Black Hole

Let's examine some more of the fascinating properties of black holes. Suppose that in the future, we took a trip in a spaceship to a black hole formed as a remnant of a supernova. If the black hole was isolated from interstellar nebulae, we wouldn't see anything much at all as we came close to it and "parked" our spaceship in an orbit at about the distance the Earth is from the sun. We would sense its presence only through its gravitational field, which would have the same strength as that of a star with the same mass as the black hole. In fact, some of the original star's outer planets might have survived the supernova explosion, and they would still be orbiting the black hole.

We now don a spacesuit with its own life-support and propulsion equipment and begin to adjust our orbital speed so that we can fall straight in towards the black hole. The first thing we begin to notice as we get closer to the event horizon is a stretching sensation. The force of gravity due to a planet or star falls off as the square of the distance from the center of the object. So, when I stand on Earth, my feet are being pulled downward more strongly than my head is, which results in an overall stretching (or "tidal") force on my body. The effect is negligible with the Earth's relatively weak gravity, but the closer one approaches to a black hole, the stronger this stretching effect becomes. We can minimize it by turning ourselves so that we aren't jumping in feet first, but rather in a horizontal orientation.

Having made the tidal effect tolerable for the moment, we look around and notice that all the stars we can see are beginning to look a little bluer than normal. We decide to radio back our findings to our orbiting ship and get no response. Then we remember that light (or radio waves) moving away from a black hole will be redshifted to a longer wavelength. So, we adjust our radio transmitter to compensate and try again. This time we make contact, but soon we lose contact again as we continue to fall in closer and the strength of the black hole's gravity increases. Our partners in the spaceship find that they can monitor our radio transmissions by continuously tuning their receiver to longer and longer wavelengths. As they try to keep us in view with a telescope on board the spaceship, they observe that we're looking reddish, and a little bit blurry. Meanwhile, the stretching sensation is building up again and is getting uncomfortable. We regard wisdom as the better part of valor and decide to rocket back to the spaceship before things get worse.

To continue the experiment, we release an instrument package to fall in towards the black hole's event horizon and to send back information as long as possible. Unfortunately, when the probe is a little closer than our bailout location, it stops working, and we see is that it has begun to stretch apart. The probe is undergoing the inevitable process of "spaghettification," and it will eventually become a long string of atoms by the time it reaches the event horizon. If, however, it could survive, one other effect would be of interest: the passage of time for the infalling probe would slow down compared to the flow of time in the spaceship. As viewed from the spaceship, a clock on the probe would tick slower and slower until it ticked no more when the probe reached the black hole's event horizon. This is because from the point of view of the outside universe, time stops at the event horizon of any black hole.

What about from the perspective of someone at the event horizon? If a person could survive falling into the event horizon, he would see the entire future history of the universe sweep by into the infinite future at the moment of reaching the event horizon. A person falling into a supermassive black hole, such as is found at the centers of some galaxies, could actually reach the event horizon unharmed. Unfortunately for the person, however, he could not get away from the event horizon, but would be swept in towards the core with its nearly infinite density (the singularity) in the center of the black hole. Although an outside observer would theoretically see time stop and objects forever paused at the event horizon, the person falling into the black hole would swiftly pass through the event horizon (moving now at the speed of light) on their way to destruction at the center.

Black holes remind us of the delicate balance within the forces of nature. The universe needs the force of gravity to coalesce gases together in order to form galaxies and stars to give light, but too much matter packed together in one place results in gravity forming a black hole from which no light emerges. Black holes also show us that our universe is not cyclical or eternal, for the formation of black holes is not reversible.

Black holes also spur us on to further understand the laws of physics of our universe, for although the general theory of relativity adequately describes and predicts the external properties of black holes, the conditions at the center of a black hole defy our current understanding of physics. Interestingly, the conditions at the beginning of our universe were similar to those at the center of a black hole, so a theory of physics which accurately described the center of a black hole might also help us understand the first moments in the history of our universe. The needed theory would be a combination of quantum mechanics and gravity, accurately describing a state of matter with ultra-high mass in an ultra-small volume. Einstein sought to formulate such a theory, and many others have worked on it since his day, but so far to no avail. Undiscovered frontiers in science keep things interesting, and who knows when another young Einstein might surprise the world with the needed breakthrough.

Summary and Reflection

One of the most fascinating things astronomers have learned about our universe is that it has changed so dramatically over the course of its history. The universe is a dynamic place, and it's on a definite, even predictable trajectory of transformation. There was a beginning of space and time. There were photons. There was hydrogen and helium. Stars formed, and with them whole galaxies. Galaxies stretch ever farther apart one from another on the spreading fabric of space. Heavier elements were born in the core of stars. These elements were dispersed through showy stellar explosions, and then the elements coalesced into other stars with their planets. At least one of these, Earth, had all the right stuff for an ecosystem brimming with livings things strange and wonderful. And without precision tuning at the level of cosmology, physics, chemistry, and geology, such life wouldn't be possible.

Whether our planet's initial formation resulted purely from the laws of nature unfolding from the initial conditions of the universe, or whether some additional guidance towards that goal was required along the way, I cannot say. Either way, the Earth and its place in the universe are stunningly well suited for sustaining life over the course of its history. And this is thanks in great part to various finely tuned features baked into the cosmic recipe from the beginning. Having studied the evidence, it appears to me that the universe was consciously designed so as to allow the laws of nature to carry forward as far as possible the process of establishing a planetary home for life.

7. EARTH, DREAM HOME FOR LIFE

I T'S EASY TO COMPLAIN ABOUT HOT DAYS AND COLD DAYS, DROUGHTS and floods and pestilence. Those are real hardships for millions of people here on planet Earth. But modern astronomy has given us another perspective on the big blue marble. Not a glass-half-full view, but a glass-astonishingly-close-to-full view. Earth has its warts—its dangers to life and limb. But compared to every other planet or moon we've been able to detect, it's in a league of its own.[1] Millions of different species inhabit our planet, on its land and in its waters. Earth is the only place in the real estate of our solar system where we humans could live without a sophisticated life-support system.

Earth is amazing. So too is the process that led to its present form. Studies of the properties of our neighboring planets have guided astronomers in their understanding of how planets form. The process begins with a disk of gas and dust rotating around a protostar. To gain further insight into the planet-building process, astronomers start by noting the main ingredients of our own solar system. One thing we note is that all planets orbit in the same direction and nearly in the same plane around the sun (all planets orbit counterclockwise, as viewed from above the Earth's north pole). Also obvious is the fact that two basic types of planets orbit our sun. In the inner solar system, we have the terrestrial planets, similar to Earth in composition, and in the outer Solar System we find the gas giants, or Jovian planets. A beginning point for any successful theory of the origin of our solar system needs to explain these and other features.

One theory is called the condensation model. After the earliest times of the universe, interstellar gases that have gravitationally collapsed into a rotating disk around a protostar contain a small percentage (about 2%) of elements heavier than hydrogen and helium. These elements could participate in the initial stages of planet formation, but only if they condense out of the vapor phase into solid grains of material. As it turns out, the condensation model neatly explains why we have gas giants among the outer planets, and terrestrial planets closer in.

To illustrate how, let's begin closer to home. Water vapor exists in the air around us, but we can't capture water from the air by just waving our hands through it. The water vapor needs to condense first, and that requires a lower temperature. During summer in the Midwest, a glass of iced tea is a popular refreshment, and after filling a glass with iced tea, one soon finds that the outside of the glass is dripping with moisture. Water vapor from the air has condensed on the cold surface of the glass.

As I edit this chapter, I'm at a restaurant where I have a cup of cold water and a cup of hot coffee on my table. My water glass is wet to the touch, but the outside of my coffee cup is dry—the temperature of that surface is too high to cause the condensation of water vapor.

The disk of gas rotating around a protostar contains various substances in the vapor phase that have different condensation temperatures. Some substances will only condense in the outer reaches of the disk, where it's cooler. Others can condense even in the inner region of the disk, where temperatures are higher. Three different types of materials within the gas cloud that lead to planet formation are typically considered. These are metals, silicates (rocky materials), and ices (including water ice, methane ice, and ammonia ice).

The ices can only condense in the outer, cooler region of the rotating disk of gas, beyond what is called the "ice line."[2] The metals and silicates can condense there and also in the higher temperatures of the inner region. This helps explain why we have gas giants among the outer planets, and terrestrial planets closer in.

Planets can form only out of materials that have condensed, so the inner planets become primarily rocky, metallic worlds, while the outer planets contain more ices, as well as some silicates and metals. Typically, the abundance of condensed ices in the outer, cooler region of the proto-planetary disk is much higher than that of the metals and silicates in the inner, hotter region.[3] The richer outer region allows the planets there to grow much larger than the ones in the inner region, where the condensed materials are sparser.

The process of planet formation from the condensed grains of material orbiting around a protostar can be likened to rolling a snowball. Just as snowballs grow in size as they are rolled through the snow, planetesimals grow by accretion of the condensed material as they orbit around the protostar. When planetesimals are at least the size of a large asteroid (one kilometer across, or so), they can attract smaller objects onto themselves with the help of their own gravitational fields.[4] Further collisions between individual planetesimals break some of them apart, while others combine into even larger objects.

The outer planets grow larger faster because they orbit in a richer region of condensed material. Their average densities are lower, however, since they primarily form from the lower density ices that are richly available in the outer region. If the outer planets grow massive enough, their gravity grows strong enough to attract and hold hydrogen and helium gases, which are quite abundant in the rotating nebula. Once such a planet reaches that critical mass, it gains additional mass quickly, resulting in gas giants like Jupiter and Saturn. (Jupiter became so large that it has more mass than all the other planets in the solar system combined.)

Alien Planets

THE STORY of planet formation is more complicated than described in this brief outline. Some of the details of planet-building theory are being re-evaluated as new data becomes available through the discovery of planets orbiting around other stars. The study of these "exoplanets" continues to be a hot topic in astronomy. The first one was discovered in 1995, and since then more than 4,300 others have been detected.[5]

The vast majority of these planets have not been seen visually—they are too small and too far away, and are usually lost in the glare of their host star. Instead, to detect exoplanets astronomers typically use one of two indirect techniques. The first looks for slight, repetitious wobbles in a star's position, observed by the Doppler effect. The other method is to look for temporary, repetitious reductions in a star's brightness. Such mini-stellar eclipses occur if a planet passes in front of its star, as viewed from Earth. When a planet's orbital plane aligns with our line of sight, it will eclipse part of its host star's light each time it orbits around. Both of these methods more easily detect large planets orbiting close to their parent stars, so not surprisingly, most of the exoplanets found are large ones. But even taking this selection bias into account, the findings seem to challenge some aspects of the model of planetary formation described above.

Theory suggests that massive planets like Jupiter should form in the outer region of a stellar system. So how do we explain the presence of massive planets orbiting close-in to their host stars? Observations of exoplanets have led to the realization that the development of planetary systems is more dynamic than originally thought. For example, orbital friction within the proto-planetary disk may cause the orbits of large outer planets to decay to smaller orbits. It is fortunate for Earth that our solar system was cleared of friction-producing dust and gas at just the right time—after the planets had formed, but before orbital decay became serious. If Jupiter's orbit, along with other outer planets, had permanently decayed into the inner solar system, the early Earth would have probably been flung from its ideally positioned orbit by the gravitational perturbance of these more massive planets.

As instrumentation and techniques for detecting planets become more sensitive, smaller planets, on the order of the size of Earth, are also being detected. For many astronomers, those are the real prize because it's widely believed that only terrestrial planets roughly the size of Earth could host advanced life. And for many astronomers, the search for exoplanets is ultimately the search for extra-terrestrial life. Finding Earth-like planets orbiting at the right distance from the right type of star would be an important first step.

Many other things are needed for habitability, however, which we will discuss below and in subsequent chapters.

Finding Prime Real Estate for Life

THE IDEA of advanced life on planets beyond Earth and our solar system has become so popularized through blockbuster movies and the genre of science fiction that one can almost forget that the existence of such life has never actually been established. Quite the contrary. There is no scientifically valid evidence of life outside of planet Earth. And not for lack of trying. People have spent tens of millions of dollars over several decades looking for (or listening for) some signal from an alien culture in a distant star system. Something that undoubtedly propels this ongoing search is an estimate of the expected number of intelligent alien races in our galaxy, as given by the so-called Drake equation. Astronomer Frank Drake proposed this mathematical estimate for the likelihood of extra-terrestrial life in 1961. His equation attempted to take into account factors that Drake supposed were necessary for the existence of advanced life.

In its modern form, presented in most introductory astronomy texts, the Drake equation for the number of communicating civilizations in the galaxy multiplies six factors: 1) the number of stars in our galaxy, 2) the fraction of stars that have planets, 3) the number of planets in each system that exist in the habitable zone (at the right distance from their parent star so that the planet has liquid water), 4) the fraction of suitable planets on which life begins, 5) the fraction of those planets on which life evolves to intelligence, and 6) the fraction of a star's life during which the life there is communicative (presumably via radio, or perhaps laser pulses).

We can estimate that about 200 billion stars exist in our galaxy, and it's likely that one-tenth to one-half of them have planets, and at least 1% of those planets should lie within the habitable zone.[6] So far, this is just astronomy research.

However, estimating the values of the latter three parameters in the Drake equation is a much dicier affair. What's astounding is that reputable astronomy texts will state, for example, that life begins naturally on anywhere from 1% to 100% of all suitable planets, and evolves to intelligence with the same probability.[7]

That's not merely wild guesswork; it's wild guesswork that ignores much of what astrobiologists have discovered about the cosmos in recent decades. The Drake equation ignores multitudes of factors that cumulatively downgrade any realistic estimate of hearing from E.T., at least if we must depend on purely natural process for evolving alien life.

Based on our extensive knowledge of biochemistry, scientists have been able to identify numerous physical conditions that must be met in order for life to exist and thrive on a planet. Let's look at some of those. And as is often done in selecting real estate, we will start broad and then narrow things down.

A habitable planet needs a host star, the primary source of its light and heat. However, not just any star will do. More than half of all stars are not solitary stars like our sun, but have a binary partner. Although it's possible for a stable planetary orbit to exist within a binary star system, the constraints are tight and far from conducive to establishing a stable climate on the planet.

Among solitary stars, the most common type within our galaxy is a red dwarf, with a mass as small as about 10% the mass of our sun. A modest difference in a star's mass makes a big difference in its brightness and lifespan. A star with about half the mass of our sun would only have one-tenth the sun's brightness, and a star with one-tenth the mass of our sun would shine about one thousand times less brightly.[8]

Liquid water is essential for a living planet, and if the host star's luminosity was small compared to our sun, the planet would have to orbit much closer to receive enough heat to sustain liquid water on its surface. But shifting the planet closer comes at the cost of tidally locking the planet's rotation. This has happened with the two innermost planets in our solar system, Mercury and Venus. Both have ended up with days that are months long when measured in Earth days and months. If this had happened to Earth, one side would bake while the other side froze.

On the other end of the spectrum, stars more massive than our sun become increasingly more uncommon in the galaxy, and they suffer from at least two properties disadvantageous for life. The peak luminosity of a massive star is shifted towards the ultraviolet and can be hundreds to thousands of times more intense than our sun. Intense ultraviolet light is lethal to living things. Earth's atmosphere is able to block much of the ultraviolet light our sun emits, with ozone (O_3) being perhaps its most effective molecule for UV-screening. But a larger star with far more intense bursts of ultraviolet radiation would overwhelm the atmospheric shield,[9] resulting in more UV reaching the Earth's surface, with deleterious consequences for life.

Curiously, most of the oxygen in Earth's atmosphere comes from photosynthesis of living organisms, and these in turn depend upon the existence of O_3 to act as a UV shield. It's a conundrum—which came first? Photosynthetic life to produce oxygen, or oxygen to protect early life on Earth from deadly ultraviolet radiation?

Another issue with a more massive star is that its lifespan would be shorter than our sun's ten-billion-year main sequence life. In fact, if the sun were just 1.4 times its actual mass, its main sequence lifespan would already be finished, and so would life on Earth.

Right Galactic City and Neighborhood

THE UNIVERSE contains three main types of galaxies: elliptical galaxies, irregular galaxies, and spiral galaxies like our own Milky Way. Most elliptical galaxies lack interstellar gas and dust, and are therefore done with forming new stars.[10] Giant ellipticals have radiation levels which may be unfavorable for life. Irregular galaxies typically contain young, massive stars, and would therefore have a much more intense level of life-inimical radiation. Only large spiral galaxies such as ours have sustained star formation for producing enough heavy elements to form the sort of planets where life could thrive.

We saw in the previous chapter that both the benefits and dangers posed by supernovae constrain what parts of any spiral galaxy can host habitable planets. In the galactic center, the number of stars per volume of space can be a million times greater than it is where our sun is positioned (about 26,000 light years out, or two-thirds of the way from the center of the Milky Way).[11] Increased radiation from these more densely packed stars, including a higher supernova rate, would prove dangerous, and even lethal, for life on any planet in that region.[12] Conversely, stars farther from the galactic center than our sun likely would lack sufficient heavy elements, thereby diminishing the probability of forming terrestrial-type planets.[13]

There are additional galactic "real estate" factors we haven't yet mentioned. Stars revolve around the galactic center similar to how planets revolve around a star. Our sun takes about 230 million years to complete one orbit around the center of the Milky Way.[14] The enormous spiral arms of our galaxy also rotate around the center of the galaxy, but at a different rate than most of the stars. The spiral arm structures are actually galactic-scale pressure waves, which can compress the interstellar gases to trigger new star formation.[15] Therefore, the region within a spiral arm is more hazardous to long-term planetary life due to greater levels of radiation from newly formed massive stars and their spectacular supernova finales. Our sun orbits between two spiral arms and at an ideal distance from the galactic center, known as the "galactic co-rotation radius," which keeps it out of any spiral arm regions for nearly as long as possible.[16]

Combine this factor with others we've discussed, such as needing to have the right kind of star, avoiding binary star systems, getting the right kind of planet at the right distance from its host star, and combine those with various other constraints we haven't yet discussed, and it's becoming increasingly clear that truly habitable planets are likely to be exceedingly rare among the stars in our galaxy. It may even be that, due to the growing list of requirements for long-term habitability, there is only one habitable planet in our galaxy—ours.[17]

In the sections to follow we will look at several more conditions necessary for sustaining planetary habitability over the long haul, as Earth has done.

Bombarding Earth

IF THE requirements for forming a habitable planet converge and such a planet does coalesce from star dust, what then? What would a newly formed Earth look like? Simply put, hellish. The energy released as massive planetesimals collided together to build the planet up to near its present mass would have melted the entire planet. Over time, as heat radiated into space, the planet's surface would have cooled sufficiently to solidify, but ongoing collisions with stray planetary material still orbiting the sun would have released enough energy to cause repeated melting of portions of the Earth's surface.[18]

In the early history of our planet, this period of bombardment tapered off over several hundred million years. But then an orbital resonance between the giant planets Jupiter and Saturn caused a dramatic spike between 3.8 and 4.1 billion years ago. The Jupiter-Saturn resonance propelled huge amounts of leftover planetary debris inward towards the terrestrial planets.[19] The severity of the impacts during this period had the effect of again totally melting the Earth's crust.[20]

Stable conditions for life could not have prevailed until the Earth's surface re-solidified at the end of the late heavy bombardment period, about 3.8 billion years ago.[21] Remarkably, the earliest evidence for life on Earth (in the form of single-celled bacteria and inferred from carbon isotope analysis) suggests that life here stretches back to about 3.85 billion years ago.[22] The takeaway from this evidence is that, within the margin of error of these estimates, microscopic life emerged almost immediately after the bombardment. (Chapters 8 and 9 will look at the challenge this poses for unguided origin-of-life scenarios.)

Due to erosion and tectonic plate movements, the Earth's surface today shows no visible scars from the bombardment it suffered early in its history. The heavily cratered moon, however, bears witness to the violence of that impact period. Due to the moon's smaller mass (it is eighty-one times less massive than the Earth), it lacks sufficient gravity to hold onto an atmosphere, eliminating the various effects of surface erosion found on Earth. Geological activity is also absent on the moon, so the craters formed during its early history still remain in place today. The airless planet Mercury bears record of a similar history. It shows the scar of an extraordinary impact of such magnitude that it left a crater stretching across more than a fourth of Mercury's diameter.[23] Impact events tell us that the process of planet formation can involve both gradual and catastrophic processes. We aren't used to thinking of catastrophic events as beneficial things, but one doozy of a catastrophe in the history of the Earth well may have been crucial to its later habitability.

Earth's Adopted Daughter

SINCE THE moon's overall density is significantly less than the Earth's density, scientists do not believe that the moon formed along with the Earth. The most well-accepted theory is that our moon formed from a single giant impact when a Mars-sized planetesimal smashed into the Earth a few tens of millions of years after the Earth began forming. This cataclysmic event would have ejected material from the Earth's crust and the impactor out into space. Computer models show the ejected material eventually accreting together to form the moon.[24]

As devastating as this giant impact event may seem, astronomers recognize that without it we probably wouldn't be here today. The moon-forming impact also increased the mass of the Earth's metallic core sufficiently to maintain two essential ingredients for sustaining life—a magnetic field and long-term plate tectonics. Earth's magnetic field is really a magnetic shield, safeguarding our currently rather thin atmosphere from gradually being sputtered away by the solar wind.[25] Plate tectonics, the gradual movement of sections of the Earth's crust, is driven by heat arising from the core of our planet. The Earth's core is still very hot, with its temperature maintained by energy released from the radioactive decay of certain heavy elements, particularly isotopes of uranium, thorium, and potassium.

Surprisingly, the core of the Earth is as hot as the surface of the sun.[26] The geological activities of our planet, including plate tectonics and volcanism, are recognized as essential characteristics for a planet to maintain long-term habitability. Both of these geological processes play an important role in maintaining a stable climate via a mechanism known as the CO_2 cycle.[27]

Atmospheric carbon dioxide (CO_2) acts to trap the sun's heat in a greenhouse effect on Earth. There is concern about modern industrial society pumping too much CO_2 into our atmosphere from the burning of fossil fuels, but we do need some CO_2. Plants breathe it, and it keeps the planet from getting too cold. The natural recycling of CO_2 within the atmosphere occurs as rainwater precipitates it onto the continents, where the runoff carries minerals to the oceans. The minerals then further combine with CO_2 dissolved in the seawater to form carbonates such as limestone, which build up on the ocean floor. But what if the CO_2 just kept building up in the oceans? Eventually we'd have too little in the atmosphere. Fortunately, Earth has its own CO_2 recycling program that helps to stabilize our climate. Tectonic plate movements gradually bury the ocean floor material deeper under the crust, where heat from the core eventually releases its CO_2 back into the atmosphere through volcanic outgassing.

The first step in the whole process of the CO_2 cycle is dependent upon the atmospheric temperature—the warmer it is, the more evaporation of water and precipitation occurs. Greater precipitation removes more CO_2 from the atmosphere, resulting in a decreased greenhouse effect and a lower overall temperature.[28]

The action of plate tectonics is as slow as continental drift, so it can take about sixty million years to complete the overall cycle.[29] Plate tectonics, driven by the heat of the radioactive decay of heavy elements within Earth's core, is the key feature of this CO_2 cycle. Without the well-timed impact which formed our moon, the Earth's core might not have had a sufficient mass of heavy elements for plate tectonics to help sustain climate stability over the Earth's history. Earth could have ended up a frigid, barren wasteland like Mars, or a suffocating hothouse like Venus. Instead, our home planet has sustained habitable conditions for nearly four billion years.[30]

Earth's Axial Tilt

ANOTHER POSITIVE outcome of the giant impact which formed our moon relates to the long-term stability of Earth's moderate seasonal changes throughout the year. "What causes Earth's seasons?" is a standard question asked in introductory astronomy classes. The primary feature responsible for changing temperatures over the course of a year is the slight, 23.5 degree tilt of the Earth's rotation axis. If Earth's rotation axis had no tilt (so that the axis was perpendicular to the plane of the Earth's orbit around the sun), no seasonal changes would occur anywhere on Earth. The equatorial zone would be overly hot, and the polar regions would never experience even a mild summer. The absence of any warming in the polar regions would allow snow and ice to build up, producing a cooling effect. Ice and snow reflect more sunlight, which would lead to more cooling, and thereby ice, et cetera—a dangerous feedback loop. In short, more of the Earth's surface would have extreme temperatures year round, with the overall effect being a colder, icier planet.[31]

On the other hand, if Earth's rotational axis was tilted substantially more than it is, the seasonal changes would become more severe. As an example within our own solar system, the planet Uranus's axial tilt is ninety-eight degrees, meaning it rotates on its side as it orbits the sun, giving half the planet an entire season of darkness while the other half is exposed to an entire season of direct sunlight. If such conditions prevailed on Earth, advanced life would be hard-pressed to survive.

Scientists have determined that without our moon, Earth's axial tilt would have varied more widely throughout its history, causing climate chaos far beyond what any ice age or global warming threat might produce.[32]

Not just any moon will do, either, for our planet's livability. The moons of most planets are far less massive relative to their planet's mass than is the case for Earth and its moon. A smaller moon means less gravitational force to stabilize the planet's axial tilt. Greater variation in the axial tilt means greater variation in climate.

Longer Days, Receding Moon

WE'RE ALL familiar with a twenty-four hour day, but if we could travel back in time, we'd find the days were much shorter. The tidal action of the moon on Earth has dramatically slowed Earth's rotation rate through the years. Early in its history, a day on Earth, set by its rotation period, was only about five hours. Can you imagine how unsettling it would be to have only two or three hours of daylight, followed by two or three hours of night, and so on, *ad nauseum*? Yes, maybe humans and other creatures would have adapted to that cycle just fine. But such a rapid rotational rate would translate into much higher average wind speeds, with far deadlier hurricanes and tornadoes, along with various other catastrophic effects.[33] Single-celled organisms might survive such conditions. Humans and other advanced life on the land, not so much.[34]

An Unlikely World

SO FAR, we have considered several features in the formation process of our planet that greatly enhanced its ability to support life. Published scientific literature describes many more requirements for a habitable planet.[35]

Certain essential features for long-term habitability are fairly relaxed in their constraints. Others are much more exacting. The acceptable range for a planet's rotational-axis tilt might be satisfied by about 30% of all planets. But a planet needs to maintain a life-friendly axial tilt for millions and billions of years if evolutionary processes are to have the window of opportunity they need to work whatever magic they are capable of in order to move beyond simple organisms like algae and bacteria and build a variety of sophisticated plant and animal forms. This additional criteria for long-term stability of axial tilt is, as it turns out, far trickier for a terrestrial planet to manage, and rules out many more planets.

Combining various essential constraints for a planet with long-term habitability—planetary size and distance from host star, stable axial tilt, robust magnetic field (for protecting our atmosphere from the solar wind), right kind of atmosphere, plate tectonics, right kind of star, right place in the galaxy, right kind of galaxy, et cetera—and estimating the probability of each of these can yield a low probability for the chance formation of even one long-term habitable planet.

If other constraints discussed in the scientific literature are folded into the calculation, the resulting probability of even one Earth-like planet in the universe may become vanishingly small, even when possible interdependencies between the constraints are taken into account.[36] As David Walham puts it in his 2014 book *Lucky Planet*, "I no longer have doubts. The evidence points toward Earth being a very peculiar place; perhaps the only highly habitable planet we will ever find."[37]

Much is still unknown about the probabilities plugged into such calculations. And there are debates about which criteria should be viewed as separate and which are simply other ways of approaching a given constraint. We will have much better estimates in a few decades as more data flows in from some spectacular telescopes and other detection devices that will be coming on line in the next few years. Our knowledge of extra-solar planets and planetary habitability is truly in its infancy. But if the odds of getting even one habitable planet in the universe does turn out to be vanishingly small, what are the implications of that discovery? Does it not suggest the possibility that purposive design played a role in Earth being such a hospitable planet for life?

Astrobiologist Guillermo Gonzalez and philosopher Jay Richards delineated another line of evidence pointing in this direction in their book *The Privileged Planet: How Our Place in the Cosmos is Designed for Discovery*. They detailed how a long list of habitability constraints—both planetary and cosmic—also make our cosmos, and our place in the cosmos, better suited for making a range of scientific discoveries. These factors include:

- Perfect solar eclipses to view the sun's chromosphere, requiring the life-friendly planetary conditions of a host star of the right size and distance and a large moon—a sun and moon that, curiously, are the same apparent size as seen from the Earth's surface.

- A sufficiently stable climate to maintain life and polar ice deposits to record and preserve Earth's environmental conditions.

- An atmosphere that blocks most damaging wavelengths of light but allows in life-friendly visible light in a way that allows life to thrive and us to view planets, stars, and galaxies.

- Location between spiral arms and far from other stars and nebula, a good location for habitability and which enables us to see to the visible limits of the universe.

- Stable laws of physics and chemistry, fine tuned for life and, at the same time, mathematically tractable and accessible enough to be discovered.

Even if it turns out that habitability constraints for Earth-like planets leave open a reasonable chance for the occurrence of other habitable planets in the Milky Way and wider universe, we'd still have this curious correlation between habitability and discoverability. That correlation is baffling if Earth and our universe are just the random result of a purely blind process. But if our universe was designed with intelligent creatures like us in mind, by a supreme intelligence interested in us discovering the wonders of an intelligently designed universe, then such a curious correlation makes perfect sense.

Summary and Reflection

So is our privileged planet the result of something more than just blind luck? Asking such a question and reviewing the evidence in this chapter might lead someone to conclude that intelligent design played an essen-

138 / Canceled Science /

tial role. Does that mean that such an inquiry is unscientific? In fact, militant atheists have been trying to quash such discussion in university classrooms by claiming that it is not only unscientific, but that it amounts to religious proselytizing. They don't even want university science professors publicly discussing it outside the classroom.

This is evident from their treatment of astrobiologist Guillermo Gonzalez. He was an assistant professor at Iowa State University when an atheist religion professor at the university, Hector Avalos, became aware of Gonzalez's co-authored book, *The Privileged Planet: How Our Place in the Cosmos is Designed for Discovery*. Gonzalez had completed the book before he even started at Iowa State, and as he notes, he never brought his design argument into his astronomy classes. But for Avalos and others, that wasn't good enough. It just wouldn't do to have a science professor who gave any credence at all to design arguments in nature.

The mere fact that Gonzalez did was proof enough for them that he didn't understand science or the scientific method—never mind that he had one of the best records of scientific publication at Iowa State of anyone his age, and never mind that if Avalos applied that standard generally he would have to kick out of the sciences some of the great luminaries of modern science, including some Nobel laureates, since they too have testified that they see clear evidence of purpose and design in nature. These counterarguments were made, and ignored. The campaign against Gonzalez succeeded, and he was denied tenure, meaning he was out of a job by the end of the following school year.

What do you think? Should witch hunts like this be allowed in our taxpayer-funded institutions of higher learning? Should professors and students not be free to use logic to evaluate the implications of scientific evidence? Mainstream science does seek natural explanations for observed events, but when nature itself argues against a naturalistic explanation, what is the appropriate response?

Could a divine designer have arranged the initial conditions of our universe so that things came out just right, giving us our sturdily habitable planet? Would it be possible for someone with superhuman skill to stand on a beach and skillfully toss a deck of cards in the air so that they all landed on the sand in a multi-story, intricate house of cards? Could the exquisitely orchestrated big bloom we call "the big bang" result in the formation of a planet with all the necessary parameters for long-term habitability for millions of species of living creatures, an unfolding process that also loaded our cosmos, and our place within it, with a long list of advantages for making scientific discoveries near and far? Such skill and foresight seem compatible with the traditional understanding of God's attributes of great wisdom and power. Beyond that we cannot say.

The more we study the unique properties of Earth that have allowed it to sustain life over most of its geological history, and to afford humans the ability to make an astonishing range of scientific discoveries about nature, the more remarkable our home planet proves to be. The location of our planet's "real estate" within the Milky Way is ideal, positioning us within the galactic habitable zone. Our home star, the sun, possesses the right luminosity with its peak output right in the middle of the visible portion of the electromagnetic spectrum. Earth orbits our star at the right distance to maintain liquid water on its surface without needing to be too close, so that tidal locking doesn't occur. Through an unlikely accident (or by design) we acquired a large moon through a finely tuned collision process that put the polishing touches on Earth to set up just right seasonal changes. The moon-forming impact also added enough radioactive elements to keep our core warm and our geology actively circulating, and it helped clear away an overly thick early atmosphere.

All of these habitability constraints and more also enhance measurability, or to use another term, discoverability. That is, we are in a curiously advantageous situation for doing science. Does all this suggest dumb luck? Should we claim that this appearance of design is an illusion, or evidence of a designer? Decide for yourself what makes the most sense based on the evidence at hand, but let's not censor the discussion based on ill-fitting attempts to label it religious proselytization. Let's follow the scientific evidence, unintimidated by empty name-calling.

8. The Cradle of Life

WHEN WE TURN OUR GAZE UPON THE MICROSCOPIC DETAILS OF the living cell, it's almost as if another universe appears before our eyes. The molecular innerworkings of the cell are governed by the same laws of nature that prevail throughout the galaxies, but in the cell, we find complex biochemical mechanisms that far surpass even our most sophisticated technological achievements. One of the questions students often report that they would most like answered is, how did life begin?

Does science have an answer? Before we can unpack this question and explore possible answers, we need a working definition of life. What is life? What defines something as being alive? Is life just chemistry, or is it something more than chemistry? What would you say is the essence of life? Physicist Gerald Schroeder marvels at the "intricacies of life" and states that it involves "the storage, organization, and processing of information."[1] Although computers do these things too, they aren't alive in the sense we intuitively mean when we describe an organism as alive. Schroeder is describing part of what makes organisms alive, but there's more to it—much more.

Some other commonly listed characteristics of living things are reproduction, metabolism (intake of food for energy), change with time, responding to the environment, specified complexity, and the ability to die. Computers fail on some of these counts. Rocks obviously fail on several counts.

Interestingly, fire fulfills most of these characteristics. However, it doesn't possess specified complexity, maintain homeostasis, or respond to environmental changes in quite the way we have in mind when we say living things respond to their environment. A fire may "shrink" from rain or "gobble up" a field of dry grass, but it isn't responding in the way a flower turns toward the sun, a hand is snatched back from a hot stove, or a bacteria flees from a threat.

Evidence shows that single-celled life existed on Earth almost as soon as Earth's surface solidified and cooled.[2] This relatively short time frame between when conditions for life on Earth first became possible and when life first appeared is a significant finding. The laws of physics and the constraints of information theory pose substantial problems for a naturalistic origin of life within this relatively brief time frame. (More on this in subsequent chapters.) In spite of this, the strait-jacketed mentality of naturalism is forced to conclude from the early arrival of life on Earth that "the step from chemistry to biology is not especially difficult."[3] And yet it is inconceivably difficult. No natural mechanism exists to generate the vast information content of the complex biochemical systems operating within even a single-celled organism.

As we saw in the previous chapter, the overly thick atmosphere of Earth shortly after its formation was mostly removed by the enormous impact which also gave rise to our moon. The remaining, thinner atmosphere allowed light to reach the Earth's surface. But even this thinner atmosphere was most likely not often clear enough to see the sun and stars, due to the vaporization of crustal material from repeated impacts and heavy volcanic activity. It likely contained significantly more carbon dioxide (CO_2) and water vapor than our present atmosphere, and essentially no oxygen.[4] The excess water vapor eventually precipitated to form Earth's vast oceans, and most of the CO_2 was gradually absorbed into the ocean water where it formed into carbonate rocks. Researchers have concluded that without the right amount of liquid water to dissolve atmospheric CO_2, "our planet would be nearly as hot as Venus and certainly uninhabitable."[5]

Another factor that has strongly impacted Earth's climate throughout its history is the gradually increasing luminosity of our sun. Stellar models indicate that for the first billion or so years after its formation, the early sun experienced mass loss through a strong solar wind, resulting in an initial decrease in the sun's luminosity.[6] But then the ongoing buildup of denser material in its core through the fusion of hydrogen into helium caused (and still causes) a gradual increase in the sun's luminosity. Astronomers estimate that the sun's luminosity has increased over the last three billion years by about 15% since its minimum level. This fact alone would have rendered Earth uninhabitable for advanced life. But well-tuned feedback mechanisms involving Earth's crust, plate tectonics, and microbial life acted together to lower Earth's atmospheric greenhouse effect and stabilize temperatures.

Oxygen and Life

THE LACK of atmospheric oxygen on the early Earth meant that ultraviolet (UV) radiation from the sun could pass unhindered to the Earth's surface. Fortunately, today all but a minor portion of ultraviolet radiation is absorbed by our atmosphere's ozone layer (ozone is a form of oxygen). If our atmosphere wasn't such a good UV shield, planetary life would be in big trouble. In the absence of an ozone layer on the early Earth, energetic UV photons from the sun would have broken up prebiotic chemicals on the Earth's surface, frustrating any gradual, chance formation of life from chemical precursors on the surface of the Earth.

On the other hand, oxygen is a highly reactive chemical. Its presence in even small amounts in the early Earth atmosphere or as dissolved oxygen in seawater would also have acted to destroy the formation of organic molecules. This presents a paradox for the naturalistic origin-of-life scenario. Without oxygen, the formation of prebiotic chemicals is blocked by UV radiation, but with oxygen, chemical reactions with oxygen itself frustrate the chemical pathways thought by some to lead up to the first single-celled life.[7]

It's been proposed that the first life emerged in caves or deep enough in the ocean to be protected from UV radiation. But there are other challenges. The origin of life requires eight or more mutually exclusive environmental conditions. So, any viable model necessarily involves the exquisitely orchestrated transport of particular molecules through multiple distinct environments at just the right moments. All such scenarios are wildly implausible.[8]

Most of the oxygen in Earth's atmosphere gradually built up as a result of life through the process of photosynthesis within cyanobacteria, also known as "blue-green algae."[9] Prior to about two billion years ago, the low O_2 level required that early Earth bacteria metabolize anaerobically (without oxygen). For these life forms, oxygen is poisonous,[10] but they helped produce oxygen. More advanced forms of life would subsequently need this oxygen for their more energetic aerobic metabolisms.[11]

Without the advent of aerobic organisms, anaerobic life on Earth might have stalled and run into serious trouble: as anaerobic bacteria photosynthesized more and more oxygen gas (O_2), they would effectively have poisoned themselves.[12]

Even as oxygen was produced on the early Earth through photosynthesis, reactions between oxygen and minerals kept atmospheric O_2 levels quite low until these minerals became nearly saturated with oxygen. Evidence shows that then, about half a billion years ago, the rise in atmospheric O_2 levels accelerated as its production through photosynthesis began to significantly outstrip its removal.[13] Soon after this we get the Cambrian Explosion, when nearly all of the major phyla of animals (categories with distinct body plans) suddenly appeared in the fossil record.[14]

Some have proposed that this rise in O_2 actually caused the Cambrian Explosion. But while O_2 is a necessary condition for advanced metabolisms, it cannot, even in conjunction with other natural processes, create the increase in biological information necessary for new phyla.[15] (More on this in a subsequent chapter.)

Today, oxygen is essential for life, and even its continued presence in our atmosphere strongly depends on life through ongoing photosynthesis. Without photosynthesis, respiration and decay processes would deplete Earth's atmosphere of oxygen in only a few thousand years.[16] This fact highlights the sensitive, symbiotic relationship of all life on Earth.

Water and Earth's Greenhouse Gases

THE EARTH'S atmosphere today is composed primarily of nitrogen (77%) and oxygen (21%), with small amounts of water vapor and other gases. Some of these gases contribute to a natural greenhouse effect that keeps our planet warm enough to support life. Primary greenhouse gases include CO_2, methane (CH_4), and water vapor. These atmospheric gases readily transmit visible light but absorb heat from infrared radiation. Without these greenhouse gases in our atmosphere, Earth's average surface temperature would be about 50°F cooler than it is, resulting in a permanent planet-wide ice age.[17]

Water vapor in the Earth's atmosphere is of course an essential component of the evaporation-precipitation cycle. The fact that it rains over continental land masses, far from the oceans, is a feature of our planet that we should not take for granted. The properties of water that allow it to evaporate and condense within the temperature range typically found on Earth make possible our water cycle and the sustenance of living things far away from surface water sources. When I lived in the Midwest, the effectiveness of the precipitation cycle was drenchingly obvious. Even though we were many hundreds of miles inland, the prevailing winds carrying moisture from the Pacific Ocean and Gulf of Mexico provided sufficient rain for the vast farmlands that covered these states.

Water's physical properties not only sustain plant and animal life on the continents; it turns out that the molecular form of water facilitates our sense of sight. Water vapor in the atmosphere is highly absorptive of electromagnetic radiation on either side of the narrow range of the visible light portion of the spectrum. But across the range of visible light, atmospheric water vapor becomes over ten million times more transparent.[18] Without this visible light "window," the range and effectiveness of our sense of sight would be limited. Even more remarkable is that the middle of this frequency window also happens to match the part of the spectrum where the sun's luminosity is brightest.

Water and Dry Land

EARLY IN its history, Earth's oceans covered nearly the entire surface of the planet. Continental landmasses only began to form at about the end of the late heavy bombardment period (3.8–4.1 billion years ago). The fact that Earth has whole continents of dry land (more than just a few volcanic islands) is another feature of Earth easily taken for granted. Formation of the continents relies upon a balance of plate tectonics, abundant liquid surface water, and chemical reactions with crustal minerals to build up lower-density silicate materials.[19]

The growth of continents interspersed across the oceans also affected the planet by increasing tidal friction, the interplay between the gravitational force of the moon and sun and the Earth's oceans. Over time, these forces slowed Earth's rotation rate and caused the moon to move into a higher orbit.[20] As noted in Chapter 7, a slower rotation rate shifts climactic conditions on Earth towards a more favorable state for advanced life.

The appearance of dry land also opened up new habitats for non-aquatic life. Should we take dirt for granted? Perhaps not. Advanced life requires not only a stable, moderate environment, but it relies upon correct continental soil abundances of trace elements, such as potassium, selenium, zinc, and many others. The early and late bombardment of Earth by rocky and metallic planetesimals helped enrich Earth's crust with just-right abundances of these elements.[21]

Origin-of-Life Theories

ONE OF the iconic arguments for a naturalistic origin of life is the Miller-Urey experiment, performed in 1952. Stanley Miller and Harold Urey sought to reproduce the beginning stages of how life might have arisen on the early Earth. A reference to their experiment, along with a photograph of Miller next to their experimental apparatus, still appears in most astronomy textbooks.

Miller and Urey sought to reproduce the components of the early Earth atmosphere and to see what would happen if they subjected this mixture of gases to energy in the form of an electric spark (to simulate lightning), or hot silica (to simulate lava), or ultraviolet light.[22] For their experiment, they assumed an "atmosphere" made of gaseous compounds that all contained hydrogen (methane, H_2, and ammonia), a mixture chemists refer to as "reducing." Subsequent research has shown that the actual mixture of gases in the early Earth atmosphere would have been a more neutral mix of CO_2 and nitrogen, plus some water vapor.

The original Miller-Urey experiments produced a few types of amino acids, an apparently exciting result, since these are known to be the chemical building blocks of biochemical molecules. However, if one repeats the experiment with the correct mix of gases, it yields significantly fewer biologically relevant molecules.[23]

The Miller-Urey results were acclaimed as a grand breakthrough, until further research undermined their significance. The experiment's results do not support a naturalistic model for life's origin. Subsequent research has not achieved more success. As biochemist Fazale Rana states, "When more realistic conditions are employed in simulations, experiments fail to provide validation. It appears as if the atmosphere of the early Earth could not have supported the chemistry needed to form prebiotic compounds."[24]

Why, then, is the Miller-Urey experiment consistently featured in even the latest astronomy textbook chapters on the origin of life? I can only guess. It once stood as a beacon of hope for those who believed that natural processes alone could produce life out of non-living material. But nothing has come along to replace the Miller-Urey experiment, making it especially hard to give it up as a beacon of hope, even after it's been discredited.

Over the course of more than six decades of intensified origin-of-life research, efforts to demonstrate the plausibility of an unguided origin of life are proving increasingly futile. As Rana notes, "To date researchers have found neither conceivable nor realistic chemical routes from a prebiotic soup to life."[25]

Biologist Eugene Koonin remarks on the inadequacy of one of the hopeful proposals, the RNA-first mechanism for the origin of life:

> Despite considerable experimental and theoretical effort, no compelling scenarios currently exist for the origin of replication and translation, the key processes that together comprise the core of biological systems and the apparent pre-requisite of biological evolution. The RNA World concept might offer the best chance for the resolution of this conundrum but so far cannot adequately account for the emergence of an efficient RNA replicase or the translation system.[26]

The lack of substantial progress toward a solution in origin-of-life studies isn't for lack of effort, imagination, or advancing knowledge in biochemistry. Synthetic organic chemist James Tour draws this conclusion concerning origin-of-life research: "We synthetic chemists should state the obvious. The appearance of life on earth is a mystery. We are nowhere near solving this problem. The proposals offered thus far to explain life's origin make no scientific sense." Tour adds, "Origins of life (OOL) research has, to be sure, become progressively more sophisticated, but its goal—to explain the origins of life—remains as distant today as it was in 1952."[27]

Compare this lack of progress to many other fields of scientific advancement over the last seven decades. Consider electronics, for example. Someone who is at retirement age today grew up without computers, cell phones, video recordings, or the internet. A hand-held calculator wasn't available for more than two decades after Miller-Urey. But from then until now, advancements in electronic technology have made enormous progress.

We tend to take for granted the technological achievements in many fields that would have seemed like science-fiction marvels in the 1950s. Why did these fields race ahead while the origin-of-life field stalled? Maybe because it's looking for the proverbial keys under the streetlight when the keys aren't under the streetlight. Maybe life's origin wasn't a purely naturalistic affair. Maybe intelligent design was involved.

Natural Steps to Life?

THE MILLER-UREY experiment, for all its shortcomings, did manage to produce some amino acids. But amino acids, such as can sometimes form naturally, do not remotely approach the molecular complexity of even the simplest living cell. Believing otherwise is like finding a few brick-shaped rocks up on a hillside and concluding from this that buildings and whole cities arose by nothing more than the same blind forces that formed those rocks. That's an inexact analogy. All the buildings and infrastructure of a large city are substantially less sophisticated than a single-celled organism. In other words, the analogy vastly understates the great gulf between a handful of amino acids and a living cell.

Unfortunately, students who read about the Miller-Urey experiment in their first-year science classes are encouraged in the misconception that getting a few amino acids in a lab experiment is tantamount to creating life in a test tube. I even had a discussion with some atheist students at a Darwin Day event on the campus of Ball State who insisted that life had already been created artificially from scratch in the lab. They scoffed at me when I told them it wasn't so.

In reality, not even one single protein molecule has ever resulted from lab experiments similar to the Miller-Urey experiment,[28] and it's widely conceded that the Miller-Urey experiment, while historically interesting, is outdated.[29]

Proteins consist of long chains of amino acids selected from twenty varieties found in living systems. Think of these twenty different amino acid types as letters in a twenty-character biological alphabet. Typical proteins are composed of hundreds of these amino acid "letters," with each type having a unique and very specific sequence. It's akin to a software program, where not just any jumble of symbols will do, or even the right symbols in any order. The sequential arrangement of the amino acid "letters" is critically important.

The similarities to a software program or book extend further. In the same way that one could not write functional software code or a meaningful page of prose by chance (say, by getting a monkey to bang away on a keyboard), expecting to find a functional amino acid sequence by chance is impractical, even given millions or billions of years. Physicist Paul Davies explains, "It has been estimated that, left on its own, a concentrated solution of amino acids would need a volume of fluid the size of the observable universe to go against the thermodynamic tide and create a single small polypeptide spontaneously."[30] (Going against "the thermodynamic tide" means obtaining anything other than a random, useless outcome.)

Keep in mind that living things require far more complexity than a single small polypeptide. A polypeptide is built from several amino acids, and forms all or part of a protein molecule. But the simplest non-parasitic living thing requires hundreds of proteins and functional RNAs. Tour comments, "If the first cells were relatively simple, they still required at least 256 protein-coding genes. This requirement is as close to an absolute as we find in synthetic chemistry. A bacterium which encodes 1,354 proteins contains one of the smallest genomes currently known."[31]

Neither can we appeal to law-like regularities to explain the origin of life. The natural forces that bind amino acids together do not show a correspondence with the actual sequences found in proteins. This is actually a good thing for the possibility of living organisms. For if natural forces selectively bound amino acids together in a certain sequence, the resulting proteins would always only be of limited variability.[32] This would disallow living things, since life requires tens of thousands of different proteins.[33]

Indeed, the biochemical molecules found in living things include much more than proteins, and for good reason. To function, cells require numerous other types of molecules with complex, specific roles.[34] DNA codes for amino acids, which are assembled into proteins, but DNA cannot work in isolation. DNA requires an interdependent metropolis of molecular structures and mechanisms to fulfill its role as the instruction manual for life. And DNA itself can only be formed within a living cell. This leads to a "chicken and egg" problem: How can one component function or even be brought into existence without the other? One observation in all this remains consistent: life comes from life. No one has ever observed any exceptions. Naturalism disregards this strong and consistent testimony and teaches the contrary view that life came from non-life. If this is science, it is science that refuses to acknowledge the continuous witness of nature.

Some suggest that the first life was seeded here from another star system from interstellar debris. This isn't a fringe view. Someone as mainstream and respected as Nobel laureate Francis Crick, the co-discoverer of the double helix structure of DNA, published the idea in 1973.[35] There was no evidence of alien life when he made the proposal, and there's still no evidence for it today. As we saw in the previous chapter, advances in the field of astronomical research have provided a growing number of reasons to suspect that habitable planets—and therefore advanced life—are extremely rare in our galaxy, with Earth perhaps being one of a kind.

Crick proposed his idea, known as panspermia, not because of any positive evidence that alien life exists, and never mind the daunting challenge of nature safely transporting microscopic life across trillions of miles of cold, cosmic-ray-poisoned empty space. He based his hope for the spontaneous origin of extraterrestrial life on the speculation that a different chemical mix of elements on another planet would have proved more favorable than the situation on the early Earth. Crick, in other words, proposed the idea because the spontaneous origin of life on this planet appeared so implausible.

What was true then is all the more true today. Decades of intensive laboratory effort to create life from non-life—whether in realistic or unrealistic conditions—has yielded completely negative results. This, and a growing understanding of how sophisticated even single-celled life is, has thrown more cold water on the hopes of discovering a plausible naturalistic pathway from non-life to life.

Summary and Reflection

EARTH STANDS out as a finely tuned matrix for life, one that required a host of well-orchestrated contributing factors to bring such a habitable planet to fruition. Moreover, the evidence from astronomy and geology indicate that life came into existence almost as soon as Earth's crust solidified, at the end of the late heavy bombardment period. Blue-green algae then helped to prepare Earth for more advanced life by producing oxygen in the atmosphere. CO_2 levels were also thereby lowered, helping to reduce the greenhouse effect and preventing increased temperatures on Earth in response to the sun's increasing luminosity.

Both the fine tuning of planet Earth for life, and the relatively rapid appearance of life once Earth was ready to host it, suggest that something more than chance and mechanistic laws of nature were at work. The prospects of nature producing the first living cell on planet Earth appeared so daunting to atheist Francis Crick that he was reduced to suggesting that Earth's first life was seeded from some faraway planet around another star. But as we will see in the next chapter, our growing knowledge of cellular complexity, together with advances in information theory, are creating fresh challenges for the idea that blind nature has the capacity to generate life from non-life anywhere, whether on planet Earth, on the other side of the Milky Way, or in a galaxy far far away. Could the scientific evidence be showing us that for such a task, a force, a causal power, beyond mindless nature is called for?

9. Information and the Origin of Life

Off the east coast of Sweden in the Baltic Sea lies the island of Gotland. My wife and daughter and I approached it by ship, and soon were docked in the picturesque old town of Visby. We were on a trip to visit my Swedish relatives who lived in a summer home on the far side of the island. Their quaint cottage was nestled in the pine woods just a couple hundred yards from the beach. After we arrived, we couldn't wait to explore this shoreline of the Baltic Sea.

With the summer temperature in the 50s, this wasn't a beach for sunbathing. Its charm was of a different sort. The beach was completely covered with small, wave-worn stones. The constant sound of the waves washing over these stones, blending with the cries of sea gulls gliding on the wind, produced a serene sense of timelessness. The millions of rounded stones formed a mosaic restful to the mind and captivating to the eyes. After walking for some distance along the shore, I came upon an arrangement of stones that caught my eye. Stones of a darker hue were arranged in a pattern about three feet across, in the following shape: Hej på Dig.

Anyone familiar with one or more variations on the Latin writing system, including the English alphabet, would recognize this series of shapes as letters. But to anyone who knows Swedish, the arrangement communicated a message: "Hi there." Immediately I knew that out of the countless stones on the beach, these few had not been arranged by the mindless action of waves and wind. How could I know this? Intuition and experience serve us well in such circumstances, but the nature of information and the nature of natural laws also come into play.

Those same methods of reasoning also apply to the question of whether the first single-celled organism in the history of life could have arisen by chance. That's because even the simplest one-celled organism is brimming with information. Can natural forces produce the immense amount of exquisitely orchestrated data found in the cellular mechanisms of life? Attempts to argue the affirmative have appealed to dumb luck, to some unobserved natural law, or to some combination of the two. However, an accurate understanding of the known and observed laws of physics undermines luck or mysterious laws as the basis of first life.

In everyday speech, information is understood to mean facts, news, data, a message, etc. Moreover, any time we can trace information back to its source, the source always turns out to be a mind, an author. In normal experience we understand that it takes an intellect to generate new information. Does this uniform and repeated experience extend to the biological information needed for the first living organism? Those committed to philosophical naturalism respond with a ringing *no*. Are they right? To answer the question it helps to dip a toe into what is known as information theory, a branch of learning that took off in the early 1950s.

Information, Intelligence, and Uncertainty

INFORMATION THEORY provides tools for making various precise calculations of the amount of information present in cases where the information is digital or alphabetic—as with software code or with the text of a novel. In a nutshell, the quantity of information present (or encoded) is equivalent to how unlikely the arrangement of characters is to occur by chance. We can get a rough and ready sense of something's information content without resorting to a mathematical calculation. For instance, we can all intuit that the information content of the greeting "Hi" is quite low. There are only two letters in the message, after all. You could spill a box of Scrabble letters and have a realistic (if modest) hope of two of the tiles randomly spelling out the word on your first try. On the other hand, an entire novel has high information content—lots of letters and words arranged in a very particular order. Imagine dumping Scrabble letters and getting even an entire meaningful sentence. It's not going to happen.

Here's another wrinkle to calculating the amount of information in something: the information content of a system composed of many parts is low if the various parts don't have to be in a specific relation to one another for the system to exist.[1] In nature, examples of such systems would be a cloud of water molecules or a pile of dirt. Rearranging the particles of water or dirt doesn't ruin the system; if an airplane flies through a cloud, stirring it up, it's still a cloud. What this means is that a cloud doesn't have much information content.

Another type of system found in nature is an ordered system, such as a snowflake or a salt crystal. These also have a low information content. The repetitious pattern of the atoms composing the crystal can be easily specified with only a few instructions or decisions. "Stirring up" a crystal will ruin it, but it can be easily re-formed since its ordered structure follows a simple pattern. Thus, both complex but random systems, like clouds, and specific ordered systems, like snowflakes, both have low information content.

In contrast, the DNA that specifies the building instructions for a sunflower, a sparrow, or a scientist involves high information content. The sequence of nucleotide bases that composes DNA is neither random nor repetitious; it comprises the instruction set for tens of thousands of different proteins used within our cells, as well as the regulatory gene networks that govern cellular organization, embryonic development, and the entire organism's functions. In software terms, this is equivalent to millions, if not billions, of lines of sophisticated computer code.

A random sequence of a thousand letters has a low information content because a short, simple instruction suffices to guide its construction: "type any thousand-character string of English letters." An ordered, repetitious sequence, such as *ababababababababababababababababababababababababababababab*, also has a low information content because it can also be produced with a simple instruction set: "type ab twenty-five times." If the ab string were a thousand characters long, its information content would still be very small, since one could say, "Type ab 500 times." However, consider this paragraph, which is about a thousand characters long. To form this particular, meaningful message requires an instruction set that specifies each particular letter (and the spaces between letters) in the proper sequence. Any such sequence of letters in a non-repetitious pattern, conveying a meaningful message, has a higher information content than the previous two examples composed of random or repetitious letters.

You may realize that whether a sequence of letters is considered random or not depends upon the person reading it. Only a mind with sufficient intelligence can distinguish this difference. A cat looking at these pages wouldn't distinguish the random gibberish sequence from the meaningful ones. It's all gibberish to the cat (even if, yes, cats do seem to have an affinity for reading material, and will find a way to lie on your book or newspaper if allowed).

Information theorists state that there is no computer algorithm which can tell if a given sequence of letters is random or information-rich.[2] However, an intelligent mind can discern the difference according to the known rules of the language. Even an encrypted, information-rich message can be deciphered. Meaningless sequences of random coded symbols can also be identified as such through techniques used in the field of cryptography.[3] It is significant that the field of operation within the military that is devoted to information gathering and deciphering coded messages is called "intelligence." Intelligent minds are able to recognize meaningful patterns and discriminate against random or insignificant patterns.

From a purely mathematical perspective, a random arrangement can have the same information content as a specified arrangement, but the presence of intelligent observers adds another dimension to the issue. Intelligent observers can identify certain arrangements or states as meaningful or functional, and designed, and distinguish these from all other states which are discerned to be random. For example, human observers can recognize that the arrangement of atoms we call a cat or a dog is categorically and qualitatively different from the arrangement of atoms we call a mud puddle. Both might contain the same types of atoms, but we all recognize that there is something profoundly ... well, *more* about the cat or dog than the mud puddle. And we also recognize that while natural forces can easily form a mud puddle, it's only in nursery rhymes that nature rains cats and dogs.

Modern evolutionary theory has become so entrenched in our culture, however, that children are taught to believe that rain, sunshine, luck, and a mindless pinch of this and that transformed mud puddles into mammals. To pull off that trick, mindless nature would have to produce a great deal of functional, highly specific information, beginning from lifeless matter. Let's take a closer look at what the evidence says about that prospect.

Information, Natural Processes, and Time

ALTHOUGH TRADITIONALLY the sciences have been divided into separate disciplines, they are not therefore independent from one another. For the most part, there exists a hierarchical ordering of the scientific disciplines. Theories of physics must obey the laws of mathematics, and theories of chemistry must obey the laws of physics; likewise, theories of biology must obey the laws of chemistry and physics. The laws of the disciplines relating to more fundamental aspects of nature provide a framework and boundaries for the workings of each of the subsidiary disciplines.

For example, biological systems are composed of molecular interactions which follow the laws of chemistry, and these all function within the boundaries of the laws of physics. Conservation of energy (the first law of thermodynamics) applies to the process of food intake (chemical energy in), and metabolism (conversion of chemical energy into heat), and motion (conversion of chemical energy into work and waste heat). Simply put: (energy in) = (work done + heat). The traditional second law of thermodynamics also comes into play here, limiting the possible

Organism – Human
System
Organ
Tissue Type
Cells *unbelievable organells* — *CHO DNA, lipids, Proteins*

efficiency of the metabolic processes and guaranteeing an increase in the entropy of the overall system, which includes the living organism and its environment.

In a strictly naturalistic universe, we would expect life (biology) to play by the rules found in all the more fundamental scientific disciplines. Do the biological processes of living things violate any of the fundamental laws of physics? A truthful answer might have to be, "We don't know." Although scientists have mapped out biochemical mechanisms corresponding to several key processes within the cell, we could still argue that life is more than a sum of biochemical processes. The cooperative, synergistic biochemical processes within a living organism form a complex, functional whole—a living creature. The information content of even the smallest organism far exceeds the information content its constituent atoms had before they were arranged as the living creature.

For the sake of determining whether such a transition in the arrangement of atoms can naturally occur, we need to understand how the information content of a system can change over time. The physics governing how information changes with time follows from a more general development of the second law of thermodynamics within the context of quantum mechanics.

Shannon A particular amount of information eliminates a particular amount of uncertainty. For example, suppose you get lost while driving to some property in the country that a friend gave your family permission to camp on. So you pull over to get directions from a local, and he says, "Take the third right, then the fourth left, and keep going. That'll get you within a few miles of it." Well, he's eliminated some uncertainty. His information will get you closer to your goal, but you could really use more information, right? Seeing that you still look confused, he adds, "After you've made that fourth left, the property's at the third main intersection you'll come to, on the northwest corner." That additional information has eliminated more uncertainty. As long as he isn't sending you on a wild goose chase, and as long as his notion of a "main intersection" is the same as yours, you're good to go.

Now with that concept under our belt (more information = less uncertainty), let's move on. The appropriate law of nature governing how the information content of a natural system will change over time is known as the *generalized second law of thermodynamics.* Physicist Arthur Hobson gives a description of this law in terms of entropy, uncertainty, and information.[4] In general, entropy is a thermodynamic quantity that can be associated with the uncertainty an observer has with respect to the state of a system, and as we saw from the illustration above, uncertainty is essentially the inverse of information.

The generalized second law applies not only to equilibrium states, but to non-equilibrium or changing states at every instant during the process. It also applies to any variable, not just to certain thermodynamic variables. These properties distinguish the generalized second law from the traditional (or classical) second law. The essence of the generalized second law is that when considering non-equilibrium states, the final entropy must be greater than the initial entropy, which means that the final information available to an observer of a system is less than the observer's initial information.

As Hobson further explains, given an initial measurement of a system, predictions of the state of the system at a later time "cannot contain more information (but may contain less information)" than the initial data provides.[5] This remains true no matter how the initial constraints of the system are changed. This implies that no scientific examination of the initial conditions of the universe or of planet Earth could yield a naturalistic prediction of life (with its fantastically high information content) at any later time. The significance of this statement is that life cannot be a natural product of our physical universe.

Physicist Paul Davies writes, "The second law of thermodynamics insists that information can no more spring into being spontaneously than heat can flow from cold to hot."[6] However, some have posited that the information required for a living system was simply borrowed from a low-entropy source within the environment. In principle, information can be coalesced out of the environment, but not to a degree any greater than already contained within the environment. This means that the arrangement of atoms forming a living organism cannot arise by natural processes from a random (non-living) arrangement of these atoms. The reason is that the information content of even a single large protein molecule far exceeds the non-living matter within its environment. (More on this point below.)

And remember, the origin of life required far more than a single large protein molecule. It required an exquisitely orchestrated ensemble of numerous distinct protein types arranged in a self-replicating cell, an entity far exceeding the complexity of any human-engineered technology.

Natural Sources of Information?

In systems which are far from thermodynamic equilibrium, differences or gradients in various thermodynamic variables may exist within the system and between the system and the environment. It has sometimes been mistakenly assumed that these gradients could generate the information found in living systems.[7] However, while thermodynamic gradients may produce complexity, they do not generate information. The foam and froth at the bottom of a waterfall, or the clouds of ash erupting out of a volcano, represent a high level of complexity due to the thermodynamic gradients driving their production, but for information to arise, specificity must be coupled with the complexity. Biological systems are information-rich because they contain a high level of specified complexity, which thermodynamic gradients, or any other natural processes, act to destroy rather than to create.

During a non-equilibrium process, statistical fluctuations become negligibly small for systems with even more than ten particles, which easily applies for any system relevant to the origin and development of life.[8] Charles Kittel, writing on the topic of thermodynamics, considers a system composed of the number of particles in about a gram of carbon. This amount is relevant to origin-of-life scenarios since physical constraints on the need for localization of the raw ingredients leading to life mean that considering larger amounts of carbon-based ingredients wouldn't affect the outcome of this argument. Kittel emphasizes that even small statistical fluctuations from the most probable configuration of such a system (with its particles randomly mixed) will never occur in a time frame as short as the entire history of our universe.[9] This means that any appeal to statistical fluctuations as the source of new biological information flatly contradicts the physics of statistical mechanics. It is therefore not possible to have "an accumulation of information as the result of a series of discrete and incremental steps," as has been postulated.[10] Again, for systems with as many constituent atoms as biomolecules have, the information content will decrease with time, and never increase.[11]

Nonetheless, others have tried to suggest that certain natural processes can, in fact, generate new biological information. At times this opinion rests on misidentifying increasing information with decreasing thermodynamic entropy.[12] Decreasing thermodynamic entropy can only be leveraged into information if a design template and the mechanism to employ it already exist. In this case, the desired information is not being created by the action of the low-entropy energy source; it is merely being transferred from the template to an output product. An example of such a system is a printing press—it takes energy to make it run, entropy increases during the process, and information is printed. But the important point to understand is that the whole process produces no information beyond what pre-exists in the type-set template of the printing press mechanism.

Our sun is a low-entropy source of thermal energy that the Earth receives via electromagnetic radiation. This thermal energy is useful energy in the thermodynamic sense because it can be used to do work. The same is true of energy released by gravitational potential energy being converted into kinetic energy or heat. Waterfalls and solar collectors can produce energy for useful work, but they are sterile with respect to generating information.

In fact, sources of natural energy (sunlight, fire, earthquakes, hurricanes, etc.) universally destroy complex specified information, and never create it. What will happen to a painting if left outside in the elements? What happens to a magazine tossed into a mulch pile? They degrade by the actions of nature, until all traces of information disappear. Or consider an unfortunate opossum killed on a country road. Will its internal, complex biochemistry increase or decrease with time due to the effects of natural forces? We all know the answer. If not eaten by scavengers, it eventually turns to a pile of dirt.

Nature's One-Way Street

WHAT DO all natural processes have in common? The definition of a natural process is something that happens in time, naturally—according to the laws of nature. Some common examples include star formation and eventual burn-out, volcanic eruptions, erosion due to flowing water, and lightning strikes. In each of these processes (and in any natural process in which something irreversibly changes in time), the entropy of the entire system increases with time.

If you made a movie of a naturally occurring (noncyclical) process and then played it in reverse, you would see something happening that is naturally impossible. For example, imagine watching a volcanic eruption in reverse—a scenario that is so obviously impossible that it would appear comical. Any naturally possible process, when viewed in reverse, will show itself as impossible. This is a consequence of a well-known principle stating that the only thermodynamic processes occurring in nature are irreversible.[13] Water running down a mountainside and gradually carving a canyon is possible. The reverse—water running uphill and filling in a canyon—is naturally impossible.

In physics terms, the only known way to reverse a natural, noncyclical process is to do work on the system, and I suggest that this process requires an agent. We can apply this restriction to determine if a given noncyclical process is natural. The logic goes like this: *Any naturally possible noncyclical process, when viewed in reverse, will show itself as impos-*

sible. *Therefore, if a noncyclical process is found to be impossible when run in reverse, it is a naturally occurring process. And any noncyclical process determined to be possible when run in reverse is an unnatural process.*

Let's consider some examples. First, imagine a cup of hot coffee sitting on a table. If we watch it over time, we observe it cooling down to room temperature (the temperature of the room increases slightly as the coffee cools). Is this a naturally possible process? (As if we didn't know!) To test it, run the process in reverse. Start with a cup of room-temperature coffee sitting on a room-temperature table. Watch it over the course of half an hour or so as it gets hotter and hotter until it is almost boiling. Does this reverse process seem impossible? Of course. Therefore the original cooling process is a natural process.

Why does our intuition match the laws of physics in this case? It's true that seeing a cup of lukewarm coffee that absorbs heat from the air in the room until it starts boiling would violate the second law of thermodynamics. But the clue runs deeper. Such a fantastical outcome represents an extremely unlikely sequence of events in which thermal energy from a cooler reservoir (the air in the room) concentrates into a warmer reservoir (the coffee cup). The reason this doesn't happen is that it would involve a sequence of low-probability interactions between countless numbers of molecules with velocities far removed from the norm.

Here's another example. Imagine a newspaper lying in a roadside ditch. Over time it decomposes it into a pile of pulp. Now, imagine the reverse process—rain, sunlight, and wind converting a pile of pulp in a ditch into a crisp newspaper you could pick up and read. This reverse process is obviously impossible, indicating that the original process of decomposition is a natural process. The forces of nature cannot produce the newspaper information in the first place, but the information contained in the newspaper certainly can be destroyed by the forces of nature.

Let's return to the hot coffee example. Imagine that you take the room-temperature cup, immerse half of a Peltier Effect device in it, and turn it on. A Peltier device is found in car/RV travel coolers, and uses a thermoelectric effect to extract heat from its cool side and deliver it to its warm side. While not as fast or as efficient as putting the cup in the microwave and using the natural process of having a hot object warm a cold object, after a few minutes, you have an acceptably warm cup of coffee again, thanks to the heat the device extracted from the air. So it's possible to reverse the natural cooling, but it requires a different process to infuse it with heat again, something unnatural. In physics terms, it takes work plus a designed mechanism to make a natural process run backwards.

Or consider this example: A stop-action camera takes a still image of a backyard scene once a day. In the series of resulting photos, what appears to be a tree house gradually emerges, complete with a hinged door, red and white paint, and windows. Could this process occur in reverse? Sure, the same industrious parent who built the treehouse over several days could decide to take the treehouse down, gradually and in the precise reverse order he or she had constructed it in (perhaps, say, as some fiendishly drawn-out punishment for a child's misbehavior). So, in this case, the test tells us the original process was not a blind natural process constructing the treehouse but rather an intelligent agent—in this case, a human parent.

Some proposed counterexamples to the rule of irreversibility are only apparent counterexamples. Natural processes can erode a mountain into a plain. Plate tectonics can turn plains into mountains. But the processes are different. The question is whether the original process that leveled the mountain could rebuild the mountain. Obviously not.

Now, here's another process, but this time, I won't tell you if it's one with time going forward or backward. Imagine a video of a large, complex molecule, composed of thousands of atoms specifically arranged so that the molecule can carry out a useful function. As you watch, the molecule decomposes into a myriad of simpler molecules. Does this seem possible? (If you're unsure, realize that the decomposition of organic material happens continuously throughout the Earth.) So, applying our rule of nature, since the decomposition of the cell is possible, the reverse process is impossible. A myriad of simple molecules cannot assemble themselves into a large, complex molecule that has the ability to perform useful work—can't, that is, compose themselves through the very combination of law-like properties and random occurrences that led to the decomposition. Put another way, blind nature could not assemble non-living molecules into the first living cell. Instead, intelligent design was involved, much as it was in the construction of the treehouse, with the key difference being that even the simplest cell is to a treehouse as an enchanted kingdom is to a primitive outhouse—that is, vastly more complex and powerful in its capacities.

One may object that our imagined decomposition of the cell occurred in a short period of time whereas the natural process that supposedly built the first self-reproducing cell involved millions of years. But there are two problems with this counterargument. First, the rule of irreversibility doesn't care about millions and billions of years. The long odds against countering entropy at such scales utterly dwarf even such epic timescales. They aren't up to the task, not even remotely. Second, if blind nature did make the leap from non-life to a self-reproducing cell, at some point it had to make a crucial, gargantuan leap resulting in complex functional biochemistry in a very brief period of time, since even the simplest self-reproducing cell requires multiple finely tuned components that don't survive in isolation one from another.

Another counterargument is to say that the rule of irreversibility and the physics behind it take us into complex waters and that as we better understand the relevant physics and the origin of life, we will come to see that the origin of life is a special case that somehow sidesteps the rule of irreversibility. But here we are comparing various clues concerning a past event and trying to arrive at the best explanation, what in logic is known as abductive reasoning. All other things being equal, the explanation that does not violate the well-established rule of irreversibility— namely, design by an intelligent agent—is on much better ground than one that does appear to violate it.

With that in mind, let's move on to some other grounds, and see how these two competing explanations fare there.

Mother Nature's Art Gallery

WE'VE REALIZED that the biochemistry of living things represents a stupendous amount of information. It is therefore worthwhile to take the challenge of trying to identify other notable structures in the universe that have occurred naturally, and ask if any of them represent an example of natural growth of information. For the purposes of this challenge, we must only consider non-living systems, since the point in question is whether nature has produced any other information-rich systems besides life.

So, what kind of structures is nature good at producing? Stars are one outstanding example. Astronomers estimate that the universe contains at least ten billion trillion (10^{23}) stars. These formed through the gravitational collapse of clouds of gas composed mostly of hydrogen and helium. Does the natural formation of stars represent an increase in the information content of our universe? It turns out that stars have a relatively low information content. This can be understood conceptually by imagining sticking a giant heat-proof spoon into a star and stirring it up. After you pull the spoon out, what has become of the star? Have you ruined it? No, its internal fusion energy production will only be temporarily interrupted, because the laws of nature will cause it to settle back down into its former state, and it will shine just like before.

Compare this to what would happen if you stirred up a living thing, even a single cell, in such a way that you rearranged many of its atoms. You would irreparably destroy the intricate internal chemical structures within the cell, and no matter how long you waited, it would not settle into its former state. The laws of nature could not recreate what your stirring destroyed, unlike the case of the star. This helps us understand why, as noted above, a single cell has far more information content than any star and, in fact, far greater information content than all of the stars in the universe combined.

Moving closer to home, what about hurricanes with their striking spiral form? Again, such structures as these rank low on the information scale since the arrangements of the individual atoms and molecules of the air in the weather pattern are not specific or particularly complex. Rearranging the molecular components of a hurricane in countless ways will not affect its classification as a hurricane nor its destructive power. Hurricanes do assume a specific spiral shape. Kolmogorov information theory tells us that this is a low-information form, since it can be specified by a relatively short mathematical formula.[14] Try briefly describing the genome of even a single butterfly caught in that hurricane. It can't be done because the specified information content is so great.

Random Attempts at Generating Information

THE ORIGIN of the first life required a massive infusion of new information. So we can ask, how much information can random processes generate? Let's start with a toy example by considering how long it would it take random processes to successfully come up with the words "The Works of Shakespeare" and the line, "To be or not to be, that is the question." To give it a fighting chance, let's grant a typewriter, ink, and all the paper the process will ever need, along with a tireless, immortal monkey banging away at random on the typewriter. Let's also help him by stripping the typewriter of all the keys he doesn't need for the job.

Reproducing the Shakespearian words requires the monkey to happen upon the correct sixty-four-symbol sequence of twenty-six letters, one space character, and four punctuation symbols. The universe would burn out before our immortal monkey managed to randomly string together even a couple dozen of these letters in sequence.

OK, so let's give him some help. Let's say all the atoms of the Earth within one hundred miles of its surface miraculously join the monkey in the composition effort, making random attempts at a rate of one billion per second. Even with all this help, it would take longer than the age of the Earth by a factor of a trillion times a billion to generate the full sequence.

Even relatively simple bio-molecular systems far exceed the complexity and information content of the Shakespeare example. Even the simplest possible self-replicating cell does so. To suggest that random chance reactions between atoms can produce such systems in a time shorter than the age of the Earth is in serious disagreement with the known laws of mathematical physics.

Protein scientist Douglas Axe, in his book *Undeniable*, highlights the limits of random chance in this universe. The laws of physics, coupled with the finite size and age of our universe, conspire so that some life-crucial outcomes that have a very low probability of occurring are not just unlikely, but impossible without intelligent design. Generating even one fundamentally novel new protein fold is one such outcome, he argues.[15] And as Axe also argues, apart from such rigorous probability calculations based on careful laboratory work, common intuition tells us that functional mechanisms, such as internal combustion engines (or single cells, which are far more complex than any human-designed engine) do not arise in nature by blind chance.

The Natural Limits of Chance

WHAT IF we broaden our horizon and consider the probabilistic resources of the entire universe for generating the first living cell? William Dembski did just this in a Cambridge University Press monograph, *The Design Inference*.[16] To understand the idea of probabilistic resources, imagine a friend challenging you to flip an ordinary coin and get heads ten times in a row. He'll buy you dinner if you succeed. You begin trying and after a couple minutes, you've managed to get a couple of strings of three heads in a row, and even one string of four heads in a row, but those darn tails keep intruding—not surprising since for any given coin toss there's a 50% chance of getting tails. You start to give up, but your friend, who enjoys watching your seemingly futile attempts, and who doesn't understand the concept of probabilistic resources or how to calculate the odds in this case, grows cocky and raises the stakes, promising you a free trip to Hawaii if you succeed.

A free trip to Hawaii? Nice, you think. So, you grab a napkin and a pencil and quickly calculate the odds, or you text a math-geek friend for the answer. You learn that the chances of getting ten heads in a row on any attempt of ten tosses is one chance in 1,024. Long odds, but you have all day to keep trying. In other words, you have enough time and attempts, enough probabilistic resources, to tame the long odds. You manage about 1,000 flips per hour, and after two or three hours, bingo, you get ten heads in a row.

What if we're attempting something with much longer odds, but also with many more probabilistic resources? Scientists estimate that a total of 10^{80} particles exist in our universe.[17] If we assume that every one of these particles has been engaged in nothing but attempting to randomly attain a specific goal from the beginning of time until now (approximately 10^{17} seconds), and acting at the maximum rate allowable by physics (10^{43} interactions/second, limited by the Planck time, 10^{-43} second, which is the shortest possible time interval between any two events), then the probabilistic limit of what could be accomplished by chance in this universe is found by multiplying these three factors together. The net result tells us that nothing more improbable than about one in 10^{140} could be expected to happen by chance in our universe.[18]

It is instructive to compare this limit with the probability of forming just one moderate-sized protein molecule (consisting of 150 amino acids in sequence) by chance. This has been calculated[19] as 1 chance in 10^{164}. This means that just this one protein molecule could not be expected to form by chance even if the universe were many billions of times older than it is and spent all its time and all its particles working on the problem. Stephen Meyer, in his book *Signature in the Cell*, memorably expresses the challenge:

> If every event in the universe over its entire history were devoted to producing combinations of amino acids of the correct length in a prebiotic soup (an extravagantly generous and even absurd assumption), the number of combinations thus produced would still represent a tiny fraction— roughly 1 out of a trillion trillion—of the total number of events needed

to have a 50 percent chance of generating a functional protein—*any* functional protein of modest length by chance alone.[20]

And a single protein is only a small fraction of what's needed to build a self-reproducing cell. From this we see that it's not unreasonable to conclude that known physics, in conjunction with the finite limits of chance within our universe, rule out any natural origin of the vastly complex biomolecular metropolis found within even the simplest single-celled organism.

This conclusion presses us to consider alternatives to chance for the origin of life. If it's not chance that produces life from nonlife, then perhaps it's some natural mechanism that succeeds at the task. However, the generalized second law of thermodynamics rules out any systematic increase in the information content of the universe, by any natural mechanism.

Paul Davies, in his book *The Fifth Miracle*, acknowledges the difficulty of explaining in a manner consistent with the laws of physics "the mystery of where biological information comes from."[21] Having taken these genuine roadblocks to abiogenesis seriously, and yet being reluctant to acknowledge a miracle for the origin of life, what else is left to consider? Davies takes the escape route of proposing a new type of physical law, an "emergent law of complexity" that can accomplish what none of the known laws of physics can do—create information. Apart from violating already established principles of statistical thermodynamics and information theory, such a hypothetical "law" lacks the key feature of all accepted laws of nature: verification through repeated observations and experiments.

New Information after the Origin of Life

WHAT IF we simply set aside the origin of the first living cell as an unsolved mystery and focus where neo-Darwinists have focused their energies—on explaining the origin of the new biological information after the origin of the first life—that is, the reams of new genetic coding necessary for the great diversity of living forms in the history of life on

Earth? After all, every novel plant or animal form needs novel genetic information. The DNA "program" for a bonobo isn't the same as that for a banana, and that for a banana isn't the same as that for a bacteria, even if there is a good bit of "software" that gets repurposed from one biological form to another. The analysis above would seem to rule out nature's ability to generate significant quantities of new information, but if we start from one or more living forms, could blind evolution find its way forward?

First, let's get a sense of how much new information we're talking about here. Let's go with a very conservative estimate by restricting our gaze to just one key component of any living system—proteins. Proteins are essential molecular structures within the metropolis of the cell, and tens of thousands of different kinds of proteins are necessary ingredients within the human body.[22] There are no law-like processes that can write the aperiodic and specific software code essential for life. What about chance? Scientists have calculated[23] the improbability of chance forming all of these different types of proteins necessary for just a single-celled organism, and it's an extremely small probability of approximately one out of $10^{40,000}$. (That second number is a 1 followed by 40,000 zeroes.) In practical terms, this means no chance.

Modern evolutionary theory purports to sidestep such restrictions by the artifice of a ratchet. Natural selection admits any random mutations into the gene pool of a species that prove to be advantageous for survival. Each such mutation might be in itself a minor affair, often nothing more than a single point mutation in a string of DNA letters. But by preserving changes that confer a reproductive advantage, natural selection is said to gradually ratchet up the information content of a genome over thousands and millions of years, eventually generating enough new information to build new bio-functionality and morphology.

Richard Dawkins describes this gradual process of conquering the daunting odds as "climbing Mount Improbable." He acknowledges this outcome as hopeless for chance actions to accomplish in one mighty probabilistic leap.[24] But Darwinism, he says, finds a gentle slope on the backside of this mountain of improbability, up which it can crawl (or ratchet) from slimy beginnings to the top of the evolutionary pinnacle by modest individual steps thought not to over-tax the natural abilities of chance. If this gentle slope exists, we could estimate the minimum time it would take for chance to produce all the different proteins needed for any new form of life beyond the first.

To consider a simple example, imagine a much more modest outcome that has a one in ten chance of occurring in a single step. Alternatively, if a "gentle slope" process leading to this outcome consists of ten small steps, and we allow that each attempt at achieving an individual step has a 100% chance of succeeding, then the result will certainly be reached with a minimum of ten attempts, which would complete the ten-step process. If each step has substantially less than a 100% chance of occurring with each attempt, then more than ten attempts likely will be required to attain the goal.

How do we know the number of small steps it might take to achieve the final goal? We don't, but it is logical that any step that represents "progress" towards the goal would have to be preserved and then built upon to attain the next small step. If the intermediate step is degraded or destroyed by subsequent random events, then the whole process loses ground. A truly self-replicating biomolecular mechanism that could survive random environmental degradation would take a big step, with very low probability. So, to imagine it happening by chance, we're back to hoping it can occur by many small steps. In this way, we again are faced with an inordinate number of small steps. How likely would such a process be?

Applying this reasoning to the chance formation of a single cell, which has an estimated improbability of 1 chance in $10^{40,000}$, we could imagine it being formed randomly with a minimum of $10^{40,000}$ small easy steps,[25] whereby a blind search would have succeeded in building the full complement of proteins necessary for constructing a single cell. So, how long would that take, assuming each small, easy step in this long evolutionary climb to construct the first cell by chance succeeded? As before, let's start with planet Earth, and then pan out to consider the probabilistic resources of the entire universe.

To determine the outside maximum of the probabilistic resources of planet Earth, we can start with an estimate that in the top one hundred miles of the Earth's crust there are approximately 10^{48} atoms. So as to err on the side of generosity, let's suppose that every one of the atoms stretching a hundred miles down were employed full-time in the Darwinian endeavor of reproducing, mutating and, given enough time, producing all the proteins necessary for our existence. This is, of course, wildly over-generous, but stay with me here. In this scenario, a reasonable rate of atomic attempts at inching up Mount Improbable would be one trillion (10^{12}) steps per second per atom[26] (again, assuming that every attempt at every step is successful). At this rate, the cumulative progress of all the atoms in the top one hundred miles of the Earth's crust working together to make proteins would result in (10^{48} atoms) x (10^{12} steps per atom per second) = 10^{60} steps per second. This is a dazzling rate of progress, but even at this stupendous and wildly unrealistic rate we would need ($10^{40,000}$ steps)/10^{60} steps/sec) = $10^{39,940}$ seconds to reach the top. The entire age of the universe is only about 10^{17} seconds.

Put another way, even with this greatly over estimated cooperation of all the atoms of Earth's crust "trying" by chance to form all the proteins necessary for our existence, the time required to climb Mount Improbable by a series of small, 100% percent successful steps would exceed the age of the universe by unimaginably many times. If we get even more generous and grant the process all the probabilistic resources of the entire universe since its beginning, the odds remain unimaginably small, just as when we ran the numbers for the chance origin of a single protein. And of course, the vast majority of atoms in the universe can't participate in building up the great diversity of living forms we find around us, since most atoms are bound up in stars or drifting through space in interstellar gas clouds. The production of living cells by whatever means is reserved for those unusual places in the universe known as habitable planets.

Information, Energy, and Imps

In the latter part of the nineteenth century, well-known physicist James Clerk Maxwell introduced a thought experiment that proposed a way to bypass the second law of thermodynamics. What has become known as "Maxwell's demon" involved a little imp who sits in the middle of a box where there is a partition dividing the box in two. Gas fills the whole box, and as usual with gases, some of the molecules move faster than the average, and some slower. The imp functions as a velocity selection mechanism by opening a window in the partition whenever a fast molecule approaches his side, and closing it when slow molecules come towards the window. In this way, the imp can supposedly collect all the faster-moving molecules of gas on one side of the partition, which represents a state of higher pressure and internal energy of the gas. Thus, it seems that the imp succeeds in gaining something (energy) for nothing.

The proper way to exorcise Maxwell's demon eluded physicists until 1928, when Leo Szilard considered the connection between information and energy. He proved that the energy expended to obtain the information about which molecules to select always exceeds the energy that could be gained by the selection process.[27] The net result confirmed what we've always been taught and what we always observe in nature—*you can't get something for nothing.*

Now, let's apply this to the claims about natural selection's creative powers. Neo-Darwinism claims that a biochemical system can acquire information (more than previously existed in the system) by selecting those mutations which are favorable, and rejecting those that are not. This scenario sounds suspiciously similar to Maxwell's demon. Darwinism is based on the view that natural selection can outsmart nature and gain something for nothing. But Szilard's insight strongly suggests all such scenarios are doomed to failure.

We stated above that the imp expended more energy than he gained when trying to acquire the information necessary to select the right molecules. With natural selection, the goal is acquiring information, not energy, so it's tempting to think that given a source of energy (the sun or a deep-sea thermal vent, for example), information beyond what the system already possesses can be generated naturally. This is wrong, however. We all know that natural sources of energy destroy information rather than create it (recall the decomposing newspaper example). Energy by itself is insufficient to generate information. Only an intelligent and creative mind can create information with the expenditure of energy. (Yes, it takes energy to think.)

Summary and Reflection

As TECHNOLOGY has advanced to where we can observe the inner workings of living cells, we are confronted with a shockingly high-tech arrangement of atoms and molecules. The biomolecular metropolis inside of a cell is unlike anything observed anywhere else in nature. The arrangement of atoms in a cell is neither a random atomic jumble, nor a simple, repetitious crystalline pattern. Instead it is like the letters in a book or in a software program—mostly non-repeating, highly specific, and serving a functional end. Neither chance, nor law-like processes, nor chance and natural selection together possess the ability to generate so much novel information, even granting the entire history and breadth of the universe.

The historical sciences, including origins science, involve reasoning to the best explanation—to an explanation that offers a type of cause with the demonstrated ability to produce the effect in question. Blind natural forces have never been found to generate fundamentally new information in any significant quantity. The only known source of new information is mind—that is, intelligent design. And the information we find in the biological realm is dazzling in its sophistication. So, we would appear to have compelling evidence from nature and science pointing to a grand creative intelligence behind the origin of living things.

10. DISCOVERING NATURE'S REACH

ONE OF THE MORE DIFFICULT CHALLENGES I FACE AS A PROFESSOR is when students won't accept what is being taught because they believe they already know the answer—a different answer. This situation sometimes arises, for example, when I teach introductory astronomy. I haven't met a student who still believes that the Earth is flat or that the Earth is at the center of the solar system, but I have had a few students over the years who have expressed disbelief in the Apollo moon landings. Others may doubt the reality of antimatter, or the time dilation effects of Einstein's theory of relativity. Some have deep misunderstandings about the Big Bang model.

When students have never even heard of a certain scientific finding and have no opinion one way or the other on the matter, such as the super-massive black hole at the center of our Milky Way galaxy, it's relatively easy to teach about the topic. But it's a delicate matter when a scientific finding contradicts someone's firmly held belief. I clearly remember a few occasions when a student realized that the evidence I was presenting contradicted some aspect of his or her worldview. The angry (but at least attentive!) look on a student's face is the universal giveaway.

One might imagine that trained scientists are above such stubborn reactions, but historians of science would beg to differ. Indeed, it's a truism among this branch of historians that dominant scientific paradigms exert a powerful influence on their adherents even long after the evidence has turned against those paradigms. We can find examples of this near and far.

The Scientific Revolution

During the time known as the Renaissance, faulty conclusions about nature and the universe began to give way to more accurate views. Up until this time, educated and uneducated alike thought the earth was the center of the universe. Known as geocentrism, this view also held that anything beyond the Earth was part of the celestial realm, where perfection ruled, and the objects there orbited the Earth according to that most perfect of geometric shapes, the circle. Quasi-scientific observations of the heavens bolstered this geocentric model, since the sun, moon, and stars do appear to be revolving around the Earth.

Additional support for a stationary Earth came by noting that if the Earth were moving, then the optical effect known as parallax would cause a shift in the apparent position of the stars over the course of a year. But this parallax shift was undetectable by even the keenest observers in the age prior to good telescopes. A rational conclusion was that the Earth must not be moving. Little did the ancients realize that stellar parallax was undetectable simply because the stars are incredibly far away, too far away for this effect to be visible without a relatively powerful telescope. It wasn't until 1838 that telescopes of sufficient strength were developed to allow the first observation of stellar parallax.

Galileo was the first to use a crude telescope to obtain observational data that proved inconsistent with the geocentric model. His observations showed sunspots, which disappointed those who held to celestial perfection. He also found mountains and craters on the moon (more departures from perfection), and he plotted the motion of four moons orbiting Jupiter, showing that not everything revolved around the Earth. Galileo also detected a full set of phases of the planet Venus, which was inconsistent with geocentricism. In sum, Galileo's more accurate observations showed that this long-standing theory of how the solar system worked was incompatible with several aspects of physical reality.

The scientific community did not immediately abandon the geocentric model, however. There were also problems with the sun-centered model, (first published by Nicolaus Copernicus in 1543), problems not substantially ironed out until Johannes Kepler introduced his three laws of planetary motion between 1609 and 1619. Kepler's first law stated that planets move not on circular but elliptical orbits around the sun, and this further departure from the Aristotelean geocentric model proved key to the accuracy of the heliocentric model. Then, too, there was the force of intellectual inertia, leading scientists to cling to the dominant paradigm long after the evidence had turned against it.

Some superficial histories of this period blame the resistance on religious belief in an Earth-centered cosmos. But belief in geocentrism crossed religious and philosophical lines, and the idea was carried forward and developed by the ancient pre-Christian Greek philosopher Aristotle, a figure highly esteemed by many scholars of the Middle Ages. More fundamentally, the tendency for scientists to cling irrationally to a dying paradigm has cropped up again and again in the history of modern science, including in situations where there is no worldview issue at stake, religious or otherwise.

Fortunately for our understanding of the cosmos, the evidence eventually won out and the geocentric model gave way to the heliocentric model, followed by numerous additional breakthroughs that further enriched our understanding of the solar system, galaxy, and universe.

The Progress of Science

THE OVERALL success of the scientific method in unveiling the workings of the universe has continued into the present. Its methodology is based on the common denominator of "show me the evidence," before which appeals to this or that scientific authority must ultimately yield.

The scientific method has succeeded in sifting through many proposed theories. When things are working as they should, such theories are accepted or rejected based on how well they agree with the evidence, and how well they stack up against competing theories. Thus, the geocentric model was finally discarded only when a new theory came along that could be shown to predict the positions of the planets with greater accuracy than the old theory. Johannes Kepler is credited with allowing the evidence to lead him to abandon the nearly 2,000-year-old philosophical commitment to perfectly circular planetary orbits, and to propose instead "deformed circles"—that is, elliptical orbits. Kepler had to sacrifice the perfection of the circle, but his proposed laws of planetary motion were strikingly elegant mathematically, and they better fit the observed evidence.

Some students have gotten the idea that science is always contradicting itself by replacing old theories with new and improved ones, so they mistrust current scientific understanding. It's true that some fields of science lie at the frontiers of knowledge, and theories related to those fields may change as technology improves to allow better observations. But it's also true that much of our scientific knowledge is firmly established. The geocentric model was replaced by the sun-centered model of our solar system, and this new model isn't going anywhere. We know that the planets orbit around the sun, and our knowledge of planetary dynamics governed by the law of gravity is so precise that we can send a spacecraft on a multi-year, billion-mile journey through the solar system and have it arrive on time precisely at its destination.

Or consider the numerous electronic devices we have come to rely on in our daily lives. The computer I'm typing on now can only work because scientists have arrived at an accurate understanding of semiconductor microelectronics. We likely will make many more strides in the realm of computer science, but we will never find that our current knowledge in this field is grossly misguided.

The twentieth century saw major revolutions in physics, ushering in the revolutionary concepts of relativity and quantum mechanics. Along with these came our first functional models of the atom and the nucleus. Powerful particle accelerators gave us glimpses into the realm of the fundamental sub-atomic particles underlying the visible reality of matter. Although we have much yet to learn about why things at the atomic and subatomic level are the way they are, we can say with confidence that no future theory of the atom will completely overthrow our current models.

The "proof is in the pudding," and successful applications of atomic and molecular physics have produced a wonderful array of practical technologies in the fields of electronics, chemical engineering, and medicine, to name just a few.

More broadly, our observations of nature near and far have confirmed that the same laws and principles apply throughout space and time. (If this weren't the case, the enterprise of science would be cast into hopeless disarray.) The progress of science has taken us to the point where we not only know much about what nature *can* do, but we also know a good deal about what nature *cannot* do. Nature is limited because it is finite and constrained. Four fundamental forces of nature exist, and there are fixed laws of nature that we know are never violated by any combination of natural events.

For example, Newton's first law of motion tells us that an object in motion will move in a straight path at constant velocity unless an external force acts on it. Therefore, if we observe stars tracing out curved paths through space, we know that something, perhaps not visible in our telescopes, must be exerting a force on them. Also, from observations of the trajectories of their curved motion, and knowledge of the law of gravity, we can even calculate the mass of the unseen object that is forcing the stars to follow such a path. In this way, astronomers have deduced the presence of a supermassive black hole at the center of our galaxy with a mass of approximately four million suns. All this results from our knowing details about what nature can and cannot do.

This isn't to say there aren't still gray areas where we aren't exactly sure what nature can do. This is where new breakthroughs occur—for instance, in synthetic organic chemistry where new insights are achieved into the special properties of newly synthesized organic molecules. Or in nano-electronics, where the size of the "circuits" (which may be as small as single molecules) means that the wave nature of the electrons affect the circuit performance, leading to entirely non-classical outcomes.[1] But while there remain many gray areas, it doesn't follow that there is only ignorance of what nature can and can't do. So, for example, when we

182 / Canceled Science /

witness stars moving in curved trajectories, we know not to conclude that these stars are endowed with a special property that allows them to follow curved paths. We can safely conclude this because we know this isn't something nature can do. And the conclusion is reinforced by our recognizing something that we know could cause such curved trajectories, namely the gravity exerted by a supermassive object in the vicinity.

Darwinism under the Microscope

ACCURATE KNOWLEDGE of the laws of nature keeps us from drawing inaccurate conclusions about what nature can do. In the past, a lack of such knowledge led to educated people reaching what we now know to be false conclusions about the workings of the universe. Observation, experiment, and a willingness to follow the evidence led us out of these false views and allowed for true discoveries about the natural world. Given this historical pattern, we should be willing to subject our presuppositions about nature to ongoing scrutiny. Dogmatizing a theory only runs the risk of obstructing the advancement of scientific understanding.

Doing so, however, is all too human. Just as it was difficult to overturn the longstanding geocentric model of the universe despite mounting contrary evidence, so too has it been difficult to unseat evolutionary naturalism despite mounting evidence against it, the theory having become stubbornly ingrained in academic cultures worldwide over the past 160 years.

According to modern evolutionary theory, chance in tandem with nature's laws are said to have assembled countless millions of atoms into phenomenally complex organic molecules, and further organized these to possess all the properties of life. Then, having accomplished this, the same laws of nature are credited with causing countless specific readjustments of these molecules into more and more complex forms. At some point, these complex combinations of atoms formed into trillions of cells, becoming a self-aware being who then attempted to explain its own origin by appealing to unguided chance. That's modern evolutionary naturalism in a nutshell.

For a physicist, a theory which purports to explain some aspect of nature—say the process by which a star forms out of the interstellar nebula—must adhere to the known laws and principles of nature, and provide causally adequate steps between each stage in the proposed process under investigation. Just saying "it gradually transformed into this" doesn't fly, unless it can be shown that known forces of nature can accomplish each step of the process.

Modern Darwinism seeks to establish that random mutations, however generated, coupled with natural selection, changed a single, original species (presumably, a single-celled organism lacking a nucleus) into every species of life that has ever existed on Earth. This theory corresponds with some evidence, but it conflicts with other evidence,[2] and the conflicts are substantial. There are still no observed examples of one species gradually evolving into a distinctly different one, as Darwin envisioned. The fossil record provides not a single example of a finely graded series of intermediates from one form to a distinctly different one.[3] The closest it comes is a small handful of cases where five or so forms can be imaginatively arranged to suggest a possible evolutionary pathway. A favorite example is a series supposedly connecting a land mammal to its whale descendants, but even this cherished example has only five or six stages in what would have required many thousands of gradually evolving intermediates. Additionally, the time from purported land mammal ancestor to fully formed whale appears to be much too short based on calculations drawn from population genetics.[4] Finally, there appear to be irreducibly complex systems in whales that would make their gradual evolution impossible.[5] And the fossil record case for land mammal to whale evolution, keep in mind, is arguably one of the best of the lot. In other words, the case for it is weak, but the fossil evidence for most other evolutionary transitions appears to be even weaker.

What about detailed evolutionary pathways from one form to another—hypothetical but at least fully worked out as traversable by small chance mutations and natural selection? As William Dembski and Jonathan Wells put it, "It bears repeating that nobody has ever shown that selection can produce a new species, much less the new organs and body plans needed for macroevolution."[6]

Dembski and Wells are proponents of intelligent design, but what they are saying isn't restricted to design proponents. Franklin Harold, professor emeritus of biochemistry at Colorado State University, has kept his distance from ID, but he writes, "We must concede that there are presently no detailed Darwinian accounts of the evolution of any biochemical system, only a variety of wishful speculations."[7]

What about observational evidence of living organisms, either in the wild or in the lab? Bacteria arguably provide the best chance of demonstrating such an evolutionary event, since their vast population sizes and rapid reproduction cycles afford them heaping helpings of probabilistic resources for chance and natural selection to work with. But as British bacteriologist Alan Linton states, "Bacteria, the simplest form of independent life, are ideal for this kind of study, with generation times of twenty to thirty minutes, and populations achieved after eighteen hours. But throughout 150 years of the science of bacteriology, there is no evidence that one species of bacteria has changed into another."[8]

Indeed, as Lehigh University biochemist Michael Behe has demonstrated, studies of malaria, HIV, and a long-running and highly touted laboratory experiment involving *E. coli* bacteria show that blind evolution, while able to do some small, interesting things, cannot build anything fundamentally new, and this despite the huge population sizes and rapid generational turnover of the microbes in question.[9] In other words, although bacteria typically have a lot of opportunities to take advantage of random mutations that could help them evolve into something fundamentally new, they don't succeed in doing so.

A Culture of Just So and Don't Go

ATHEISM CLAIMS that any appearance of design in nature is unreal and that things only appear to be designed, but are not. As biologist Richard Dawkins states, "Biology is the study of complicated things that give the appearance of having been designed for a purpose."[10] Dawkins and other proponents of philosophical naturalism maintain that this insistent appearance of design must be ignored. "Biologists must constantly keep in mind that what they see was not designed, but rather evolved," writes Francis Crick.[11] In other words, don't go there.

In practical terms this has meant propping up modern evolutionary theory by a variety of evidence-starved just-so stories. For example, and as discussed above, from Darwin's time until now, the collective fossil record has shown a pervasive lack of transitional forms. The few examples seeming to fit the theory are more the exception than the rule, and even these are mere shadows of the evidence one might hope for. In response to this contrary evidence, the theory has been patched up with a new idea, unknown to Darwin—"punctuated equilibrium."[12]

This is the idea that major evolutionary innovations in the history of life occur in brief spurts, too fast to be recorded in the fossil record, spurts followed by long periods of stasis. This is like a magician who claims he can pull a rabbit out of a hat, but only when the curtain is drawn. Where is the evidence? Always off stage. No witnesses. Punctuated equilibrium is just one of several desperate stories evolutionists have been reduced to telling in order to explain away contrary evidence.

Another breakdown between evolutionary theory and the evidence is seen in the Cambrian Explosion. This major event in the history of life occurred about 520–530 million years ago, when numerous complex animals with unique and diverse body plans suddenly appeared in the fossil record. The discord between this evidence and the theory was known even to Darwin, and the problem has only grown worse as more evidence has come to light.[13]

A science journal published out of the Smithsonian Institution published a review essay detailing the mounting problems that the Cambrian explosion posed for evolutionary theory, and suggested intelligent design as a better explanation for the sudden appearance of so many animal forms.[14] The editor of the journal, Richard Sternberg, was subsequently attacked for allowing the article to be peer reviewed and published on his watch, and his position at the Smithsonian was torpedoed. Why the thuggish behavior toward an accomplished scientist otherwise in good standing with the scientific community? He did the unforgivable. He allowed evidence and arguments for intelligent design to be presented in a peer-reviewed science journal. As a result, he was "expelled"[15] by the secularist academic community. This was *cancel culture* before cancel culture was a household term, and it tells us something. If modern evolutionary theory were not held with religious fervor by many in the academic community, honestly acknowledging contrary evidence, or suggesting intelligent design as a competing possibility, would not bring charges of heresy followed by rabid attacks on a scientist's career.

Another example of evidence contrary to Darwinism is captured in the idea known as irreducible complexity. Some biological machines are irreducibly complex in that they require all of their parts to function. Where such examples are found in molecular biology, they pose a challenge. How could natural selection build the biological machine one small step at a time via random mutation and natural selection if the thing doesn't work until all of its parts are assembled? Natural selection doesn't select a biological form that isn't working. It discards it. Natural selection selects for present function and advantage, never for future function. So how could it select for the first few parts of a biological machine when they don't do something useful for the cell? In such cases, it seems to be an all-or-nothing affair.

In any case, no one in this debate who is being taken seriously claims that a single giant chance mutation could construct some of the irreducibly complex biomechanical wonders uncovered by modern-day molecular biology.[16] The odds of such a freak mega-mutation are simply too long—like dumping all the parts of a Harley Davidson motorcycle into a concrete mixing truck and the thing assembling by chance as the parts tumble about in the mixing drum. It's not going to happen.

The most famous example of irreducible complexity in molecular biology is the bacterial flagellum, a microscopic outboard motor used by some bacteria to swim. It's an engineering marvel, and researchers have recently uncovered a new layer of sophistication in the growth and regulation of its whip-like tail.[17] Take one of flagellum's many indispensable parts away and the thing becomes inoperative. Evolutionists have offered counter-arguments to this challenge, including the idea that evolutionary processes co-opted other simpler biological machines performing other functions on the way from simplest precursor to fully functioning machine. But the co-option story is long on imagination and short on both engineering detail and hard evidence. Plus, even if we presuppose that there were one or more precursor biological machines available for nature to co-opt on the evolutionary journey to finished biological machine, how likely is such a blind evolutionary journey? As we saw, studies of various microbes over several decades strongly suggest that evolutionary processes are incapable of such innovations. Information theory coupled with probability mathematics suggests much the same thing.

Do we see random mutations managing such engineering marvels in any other realm? Just the opposite. The NASA Space Shuttle Challenger provided a sobering case in point. On one mission, the failure of a single O-ring gasket led to the destruction of an extremely complex, designed system, with the tragic loss of the lives of the crew members.[18] This is the norm, and it's because engineering marvels are complex systems with carefully orchestrated interdependent parts. They're irreducibly complex. Life seems to be in the same category.

Scientism Unspun

SOME OF my fellow scientists will not even consider the possibility that molecular machines such as the bacterial flagellum were intelligently designed. For many, this unwillingness seems to be rooted in a dogmatic commitment to philosophical naturalism and its offspring, an outlook known as scientism.

If naturalism is scientism's mother, the success of the scientific enterprise is scientism's father. Scientism holds that everything can ultimately be explained by appeal to one or more natural causes, and that science is the ultimate arbiter of all truth. Science has solved many puzzles, the thinking goes; why not all of them? In essence, scientism is philosophical naturalism combined with a major ego trip for scientists.

But if everything is the result of natural forces, then even our thoughts are simply natural results of some or all of the four fundamental forces of physics working on the matter inside our heads. If that is so, then all of our thoughts are no more rational than a dust storm, a volcanic eruption, or the slow rotting of a fallen apple.

Alvin Plantinga, whose credentials have earned him a reputation as a preeminent analytic philosopher, cites what he calls "Darwin's doubt."[19] Darwin, followed by several naturalistic philosophers, acknowledged that evolutionary theory, if followed to its rational conclusion, seems to undermine faith in rationality. As Darwin put it, "With me the horrid doubt always arises whether the convictions of man's mind, which has been developed from the mind of the lower animals, are of any value or at all trustworthy. Would any one trust in the convictions of a monkey's mind, if there are any convictions in such a mind?"[20] Plantinga argues that indeed, if naturalism is true, then rationality has no foundation. The atheist philosopher Thomas Nagel has made much the same point.[21]

Natural selection, within the evolutionary paradigm, selects for reproductive fitness. But as Plantinga notes, the discovery of the laws of physics involved a level of reasoning power to discover and apply "mathematics of great depth, requiring cognitive powers going enormously beyond what is required for survival and reproduction."[22]

Physicist Paul Davies, who is not a theist, presses a similar point. Primitive man needed skills, but what survival advantage in such a context, he asks rhetorically, could possibly generate, via a series of small random mutations and natural selection, the capacity to unravel the order of the atomic realm, or to predict the existence and properties of black holes? The theoretical insights required to understand these previously unknown features of nature relied upon using advanced mathematics and making leaps of imaginative genius. "These are completely outside the domain of everyday experience," he comments, "totally surplus to requirements, not at all necessary for good Darwinian survival."[23]

If we can't trust our own thoughts, then science and philosophy are spurious at best, including the conclusion that naturalism is true. Thus does evolutionary naturalism undo itself, and with it, scientism, since scientism is founded on naturalism. Plantinga considers various attempts to rebut this conclusion and finds the attempts inadequate. His conclusion is that there is deep conflict between science and philosophical naturalism.[24]

Nature: Coy but Congenial

NATURE'S SECRETS may not be obvious, but neither are they so obscure that we cannot plumb them. The many successes generated by the scientific revolution demonstrate that in many cases we can. But why are nature's secrets at all accessible to us? It's easy to take this for granted, but Albert Einstein didn't. He marveled that the universe was comprehensible by the human mind. Plantinga, Nagel, and others show why this is difficult to explain within a naturalistic framework, but they suggest that it comports well with the Judeo-Christian doctrine of *imago dei*, the idea that humans are created in the image of a rational Creator.

For science to succeed, "there must be a match between our cognitive faculties and the world" Plantinga notes.[25] And within the theistic framework, it is to be expected that a Creator who made us in his image, with the capacity to think rationally, would design the universe and us in a complementary manner so that we might one day come to understand the universe.[26] Also, "for science to be successful, the world must display a high degree of regularity and predictability,"[27] and scientists must believe that nature is in important ways orderly and predictable. Such belief is not inevitable. It has not been shared by all cultures. "It is important to see," Plantinga adds, "that our notion of the laws of nature, crucial for contemporary science, has this origin in Christian theism."[28]

Once we comprehend the workings of the laws of nature, we do not need an explicit reference to God to employ these natural laws to our advantage, but the laws themselves need explaining, as does the fact that we have minds that can understand them. Believing that the laws of nature and their workings in the universe are the result of a rational God's design has served as inspiration for many of the most influential scientists, and indeed, was crucial to the birth of science, which occurred in only one time and place in human history—Christian Europe. Most of the great names of early Western science—Nicholas Copernicus, Galileo Galilei, Isaac Newton, Robert Boyle, John Wilkins, Roger Cotes, and many others—all were serious believers in God.[29] This by itself is no proof that Judeo-Christian theism is true. But it does mean the common atheist claim that science and Christianity are at war is a gross distortion of the historical record. Far from being at war with science, Christendom gave us science. What you make of that historical fact is up to you.

Summary and Reflection

As SCIENTIFIC understanding of our universe has progressed, some of humanity's long-held theories have proven inadequate to explain new observations of nature. For example, a more accurate view of our solar system was brought about through technological improvements in our ability to see details of celestial objects. Resulting observations forced scientists and philosophers to abandon the old geocentric theory and replace it with a model of the solar system with the sun at its center.

The theory of evolution shares characteristics in common with the geocentric model of the solar system. The geocentric model explained some things tolerably well, but it had to be jury-rigged more and more to explain away contrary evidence that continued to accumulate—in particular, the evidence of retrograde motion of planets, which did not fit at all neatly with the geocentric model. For the geocentric model, it was the convenient idea of epicycles, messy add-ons to the geocentric model that became necessary to get it to fit the data. For evolutionists, it's punctuated equilibrium, or co-option, or a dozen other highly strained just-so stories.

In this era of science, we can no longer be excused for hanging everything on a theory when its primary tenets contradict the known workings of nature. Evolution's ability to explain some things about life is not a license to assume it can explain all things about life.

The philosophical outlook known as scientism blossomed when science successfully explained many new phenomena by natural laws. It has been running on dwindling momentum, however. Evidence has been mounting that nature is insufficient to explain its own origin, the origin of life, and the origin of all the complexities of living organisms since the appearance of the first single-celled organism billions of years ago. A serious rethink is long overdue.

11. MIND, BEAUTY, AND INFORMATION

ARE OUR MINDS SIMPLY A MANIFESTATION OF ELECTROCHEMICAL activity within the physical brain, or is the mind something more, and somehow distinct from the brain? Someone has quipped, "The brain is a computer made of meat." Is that all we are, conscious meat? If you're like me, you probably feel you are something other than the approximately three pounds of gray matter inside your skull.

We recognize our dependence upon our brains. Brain damage can seriously limit the ability of a person to express themselves or to control their body or their emotions. But the personhood of the individual is not thereby reduced. Even patients in a coma, after they awaken, sometimes report that they retained awareness of their physical condition and could hear conversations around them and feel emotional responses to people in the room.

What other evidence can we bring to bear on this question of the nature of the mind and the brain? Pioneer neurosurgeon Wilder Penfield, whose brain surgery techniques helped numerous patients suffering from epilepsy, provided an unusually well-informed perspective on the distinction between the mind and the brain. In *The Mystery of the Mind* Penfield's direct observations of the human brain in conscious patients during brain surgery led him to conclude that "our being is to be explained on the basis of two fundamental elements."[1] He was referring to the mind and the brain, and he meant that the mind is distinct from the physical. In describing the relationship between the two, he wrote, "The mind seems to act independently of the brain in the same sense that a programmer acts independently of his computer, however much he may depend upon the action of that computer for certain purposes."[2]

Penfield offered several lines of evidence for this conclusion. A particularly dramatic source of evidence came from his observations during brain surgery on patients who remained conscious (a possibility since the brain itself doesn't have pain receptors). "When I have caused a conscious patient to move his hand by applying an electrode to the motor cortex of one hemisphere, I have often asked him about it," Penfield wrote. "Invariably his response was: 'I didn't do that. You did.' When I caused him to vocalize, he said: 'I didn't make that sound. You pulled it out of me.'"[3] He then adds, "There is no place in the cerebral cortex where electrical stimulation will cause a patient to believe or to decide."[4]

What this suggests is that the mind, which refers to itself as "I" or "me," stands aloof from the brain. This view is consistent with the idea, shared by many religions and even by some who do not consider themselves religious, that humans possess an immaterial soul, one that may persist after death. Penfield's conclusions about the mind/brain duality are not shared by all researchers, but his conclusions are to him the best fit with his surgical observations.

The Origin of Consciousness

Do we believe that rational thought is possible? The judicial system relies upon it in determining whether to admit evidence. Think of a detective investigating a crime who reasons, "This person couldn't himself have committed the crime, because he was seen by reliable witnesses in another city when the crime occurred." Or, to give a more technical example, suppose an astronomer concludes, "Observing a nearly complete set of the phases of the planet Venus counts strongly against the geocentric model of the solar system." In either of these cases, can we trust such reasoning? Of course we realize the importance of double-checking our facts and considering and comparing various possible explanations, but that's different from simply dismissing rational inquiry as fundamentally illusory. We may at times reason badly, but we do not thereby mistrust the existence or efficacy of reason.

There are those, however, those who do dismiss reason. "There is a thought that stops thought," wrote G. K. Chesterton.[5] It's the idea that there is no fundamental basis for reason. Such a self-destructive thought is aided and abetted by thinking nature is all that there is. If nature is only particles in the void obeying mindless regularities, where in that scenario is there any room for rational inquiry?

Chesterton wrote, "It is idle to talk always of the alternative of reason and faith. Reason is itself a matter of faith. It is an act of faith to assert that our thoughts have any relation to reality at all."[6] Thought itself requires a separateness from the mechanism of thinking. If naturalism is true, then our thoughts are not real in themselves; they are only random physical states of the molecules which make up the neurons of our brains. With such an assumption, we could not think. Our thoughts would only be interactions following the laws of nature, unguided by anything higher than the forces between atoms.

What becomes, then of "you"? Naturalism allows no identity of the individual beyond the probabilistic output of the three-pound collection of atoms between our ears. "You cannot think if you are not separate from the subject of thought," Chesterton continued. "Descartes said, 'I think; therefore I am.' The philosophic evolutionist reverses and negatives the epigram. He says, 'I am not; therefore I cannot think.'"[7]

However, what if nature is not all there is? What if mind is more than just a sort of froth on brain chemistry?

Whenever natural causes do violence to our brains, our reason is corrupted. Alcohol, drugs, brain tumors, head injuries, and neurological diseases all negatively affect our ability to reason. Is there a clue here? C. S. Lewis wrote, "When Nature, so to speak, attempts to do things to rational thoughts she only succeeds in killing them."[8] Lewis describes a "frontier" between Reason and Nature, across which Nature only comes to kill, but Reason can cross to accomplish a multitude of "unnatural" things.

He continues: "Every object you see before you at this moment—the walls, ceiling, and furniture, the book, your own washed hands and cut fingernails, bears witness to the colonization of Nature by Reason: for none of this matter would have been in these states if Nature had had her way."[9]

Our minds, in other words, are unnatural in at least one important sense: they have the ability not only to comprehend nature, but also to transform nature's elements into objects and machines that would never assemble themselves in that way. This fact is underscored by the common distinction between *natural* and *artificial*, between *nature* and *artifice*.

Years ago, I read something that brings the claims of naturalism into a stark light: Naturalism insists that hydrogen gas, given enough time, will turn into people. And since people make the technological marvels of our culture, we can extend this claim of naturalism to say that hydrogen gas, given enough time, will turn into cars, computers, and cathedrals. That's one explanation on the table. The question is whether we are willing to consider another possibility, that mind is as much behind our finely tuned, unfolding universe as it is behind cars, computers, and cathedrals—the possibility, as C.S. Lewis put it, that "human thought is... God-kindled."[10] If so, then reason has a foundation far better than hydrogen gas, far better than particles in the void.

Transported

WHEN CONSIDERING whether there is something more to reality than the physical, there is another source of experience we would do well to consider. Can you remember ever seeing or hearing something that produced an unexpected longing for a reality beyond anything you have ever actually known? In every other aspect of our lives, our desires correspond to things that would fulfill those desires. If we long for companionship, it's possible for that longing to be fulfilled. If we desire rest, we can sleep. If we are hungry, we can eat and be satisfied. But what about a longing that doesn't seem to have any fulfillment in this life? Does this mean the longing is empty, even false? Or does it suggest we are longing for something that does exist, but it's something beyond this world?

[Handwritten margin notes: "All Senses", "Sun", "Salt Air —", "Beach", "Sense", "Transcendence, God"]

A friend of mine recounts walking on a familiar path along a river through a park. The sunlight was filtering through the leaves of the trees overhead, and in that moment, she felt pierced with longing, and that there must be something beyond—a transcendent power, something or someone far greater than herself. It is easy to dismiss such an experience in others, until it happens to you. Such moments catch us by surprise and cause our hearts to ache for something more. If every type of desire has its proper fulfillment in something real, then perhaps there is "something more." One scholar has expressed it this way: "Every experience of beauty points to infinity."[11]

Defining Beauty

BOTH ARTISTICALLY and scientifically, beauty has recognizable attributes. Classically, the concept of beauty is captured in words such as harmony, proportion, and radiance.[12] In an artistic context, we are likely familiar with the concepts of harmony (meaning all the elements fit together in a unified whole) and proportion (each element is in the correct relation to the others). But the concept of radiance may be unfamiliar. Radiance is the manifestation of an inner depth of reality.[13] Radiance could be described as the difference between a doll's face and the laughing smile of a human child. The doll is hollow, but the radiance of the child's face manifests an inner depth.

In living things, beauty has invisible inner qualities and outer visible elements. To some degree, non-living things also manifest a form derived from inner, invisible properties. A sunset reflecting off a calm sea appears outwardly beautiful as a result of the invisible properties of atoms and their interactions with the spectrum of light coming from the sun.

Light itself is invisible until it interacts with matter, and matter is invisible unless it reflects the light, and we then perceive something of the "inner form" of both. This interplay between the visible and the invisible adds to the beauty we perceive and understand. Writes Thomas

Dubay: "Beauty is necessarily shrouded in mystery—which is part of its splendor."[14]

Beauty also plays a role in science, where aspects of beauty come into play. One such aspect is simplicity in the sense of "completeness and economy."[15] In a scientific theory, simplicity in this sense is seen as a virtue, with the theory capturing the truth of reality with the most succinct expression possible.

Another aspect of beauty, symmetry, is especially appealing in scientific theories and is based upon profound symmetries observed in nature. For example, translational symmetry refers to the fact that if you move in any direction, the properties of nature remain the same, leading to the important conclusion that the same laws of physics apply anywhere in the universe. In addition, symmetry properties are linked with laws of nature that describe the conservation of specific physical properties, such as angular momentum. Without these properties, our understanding of the universe would be severely curtailed.

The concept of brilliance in a scientific theory appears if the theory reveals deeper truths than just a trivial fact. In physics, for example, the de Broglie hypothesis can be written as a simple relation between the momentum of a particle and its wavelength. Although mathematically simple, its brilliance appears in that it reveals the wave-particle duality of nature and leads to the whole field of quantum mechanics, dramatically advancing our understanding of atomic-scale phenomena.

Brilliance in a scientific theory is the counterpart of radiance in the classical definition of beauty—both suggest a hidden inner depth which heightens our appreciation of the beautiful. Alvin Plantinga describes these qualities as "fruitfulness." This quality suggests that the theory can produce more than it seems to contain at first glance, similar to the remarkable potential hidden within a living seed.[16]

A Meaningful World

BENJAMIN WIKER and Jonathan Witt identify four common elements of artistic works of great beauty—depth, harmony, elegance, and radiance. They argue that these four characteristics are shared by works of artistic genius across ages and cultures.[17] They then show how nature manifests these four characteristics of artistic genius, and does so to an unparalleled degree. The challenge this poses is hard to miss. If ordinary works of human design lie beyond the capacity of blind natural forces, how much more so does the signature of genius we find in everything from the fine tuning of the laws of physics to accommodate life to the exquisite kingdom of the cell?

Seen in this light, "the universe, rather than being devoid of meaning... is like a great work of art, full to overflowing with meaning,"[18] comment Wiker and Witt. And we find such artistry at many levels of the natural world. The periodic table of the elements, for example, is ingeniously beautiful in that it "possesses depth: it's dense, rich, subtle and difficult to exhaust." At the same time, "the work is readable or, to use Thomas Aquinas's more suggestive term, it possesses clarity."[19] The comprehensibility of the elements arranged in the periodic table provides evidence that "the genius of nature is an anthropic work—a work that seems to have us in mind."[20]

We should not, however, imagine "that our own reasoning is the plumb line of the world."[21] Humility in the scientific endeavor "leads us to expect the mysterious," the unexpected. "Fruitful scientists keep their bare feet in the earth," as Wiker and Witt put it, realizing "that the text of nature goes deeper still."[22]

Beauty and Reality

OFTENTIMES WE hear it said that beauty is only "in the eye of the beholder." But Dubay maintains that "both science and theology agree on the objectivity of beauty."[23] In its characteristics of simplicity and elegance, beauty not only appeals to our minds, but also helps us identify scientific theories that correspond to reality. Physicist Paul Davies has said, "It is widely believed among scientists that beauty is a reliable guide to truth."[24]

"Beauty is the first test,"[25] says mathematician G. H. Hardy. Paul Dirac, who received the 1933 Nobel Prize in Physics, states, "The research worker, in his efforts to express the fundamental laws of nature in mathematical form, should strive mainly for mathematical beauty."[26] From a personal perspective, I can affirm that when I work on a mathematical derivation of some physical phenomenon, if the equations become simpler and more symmetrical as I proceed, my experience shows that the derivation is on the right track. On the other hand, a sign that it has gone astray is usually when the mathematics of the equations become "ugly"—that is, increasingly complicated and messy.

This relation between mathematics and physical reality hints that mathematical principles underlie the universe, and by extension, that behind the universe there is, perhaps, a mathematician. Eugene Wigner, recipient of the 1963 Nobel Prize in Physics, expresses the mathematical underpinnings of the universe as meta-natural: "The miracle of the appropriateness of the language of mathematics for the formulation of the laws of physics is a wonderful gift which we neither understand nor deserve."[27]

Physicist William Pollard shares four examples in the history of physics where new physical concepts were found to match previously developed mathematics.[28] In each case, fields of pure mathematics were initially developed without their inventors having any conception that their work had the slightest connection with the physical world. Then, sometimes several decades later, physicists who were seeking to formulate equations that described regularities in the physical world found that these previously developed fields of mathematics perfectly fit and described the aspects of physical reality under investigation. The hand-in-glove fit even allowed the physicists to correctly predict new and unknown phenomena from their theories.

Among Pollard's examples of this is the famous theory of general relativity. In formulating this theory, Einstein utilized Riemann's mathematics of curved spaces of higher dimensions, an esoteric work developed several decades earlier. The union of elegant mathematics with Einstein's profound physical insight produced a theory that predicted phenomena no one had been able to describe or even imagine before then. These predictions include the warping of space near the sun, gravitational waves, and an accurate description of black holes. The mathematics of general relativity has a flawless track record of highly accurate agreement between its predictions and observations. Einstein's general relativity theory is well-deserving of the accolade, "Probably the most beautiful of all existing theories."[29] And its success in describing unexpected aspects of nature gives strong support to beauty as a guide to truth.

In a recent critique of mathematical beauty as a guide to understanding nature, physicist Sabine Hossenfelder points out that this approach has failed to bear fruit in modern theoretical physics.[30] She asks, "Why should the laws of nature care what I find beautiful?" Why indeed? And yet it has often been so—a mystery inexplicable within the confines of naturalism.

Hossenfelder is correct that something is amiss in contemporary theoretical physics. But the failure to make significant progress on the standard model of particle physics may stem from a misguided concept of beauty. In the last few decades, naturalism's aversion to design has led to the assumption that evidence of fine tuning in physical constants is "ugly."[31] Fine tuning suggests a designing intelligence was at work, and the naturalist finds this off-putting, preferring instead to find a universe devoid of any distinctiveness that would seem to reflect a designer's act of choice.

The physics concept known as "naturalness" expects that physical parameters, when expressed in dimensionless form, should only be of order unity (meaning approximately equal to one). Hossenfelder argues that this approach has not been productive. "Naturalness, it seems, is just not correct."[32]

I suggest the solution is to discard scientism's aversion to evidence of fine tuning. Such evidence isn't ugly. It isn't something to be explained away. It's fascinating, and a whisper perhaps of a deeper reality, a sign that before there was matter and laws of matter, there was mind. The conviction that mind preceded matter was crucial to the birth of science. And we have no good reason to regard it as verboten now, precisely when the discovery of fine tuning has given us a powerful additional reason to consider it.

Beauty and the Beholder

Although beauty has an objective quality even within science, in another sense beauty *is* in the eye (or the mind) of the beholder. By this I do not mean that it is purely subjective, but that its appreciation is dependent on qualities of perception, sympathy, and intellect within the beholder. "The mere animal hears the Mozart concerto and sees the daffodil," writes Dubay, "but it is neither enraptured nor overwhelmed. It has no intellect to perceive the inner depth, the form."[33]

Besides needing a sufficient level of intellect to respond to beauty, we also need the ability to delight in something other than ourselves. Being fully responsive to beauty requires having enough humility to let something else move you. It requires the ability to appreciate a thing for what it is, not just for what use it may have. Such a quality of intellect is neither animal-like nor mechanistic.

Beauty abounds on this Earth in majestic mountains, sparkling waterfalls, pastoral landscapes, white sandy beaches splashed by turquoise-blue waves. Beauty deepens in form and variety in the living creatures which grace our planet in endless abundance: flowers of every hue and symmetric form, tropical fish, songbirds and raptors, mammals large and small, each manifesting radiant beauty.

Human art demands an artist. The artistry of the beauties of nature is surely no less than that of any painting in the Louvre. What are we to make of this? Dubay sees in this evidence of foresight and planning: "One bluebird 'in its way absolutely perfect' is staggering evidence of art and design."[34]

Depth of Form, by Design

THE FORCES of nature acting on matter according to the laws of physics often give rise to forms of beauty manifesting simplicity, symmetry, and harmony. Patterns can arise naturally that show simple, symmetric repetition of form, as in crystals. Beauty is also found in complex arrangements of matter involving a significant degree of randomness, as seen in clouds illuminated by the setting sun. Throughout the natural universe we see beautiful images revealed to us by astronomers' powerful telescopes. Diamond-like clusters of stars, vaporous nebulae of almost every conceivable color, and majestic galaxies all strike our senses as beautiful examples of celestial art.

These examples of beauty in nature, however, possess only a limited degree of depth of form. The greatest depths of beauty are in living things, such as flowers, animals of all types, and our fellow human beings. From where does the intense depth of form seen in a rose, a butterfly, or a human face arise? Hans Urs von Balthasar affirms beauty as arising from within the form: "The beautiful is above all a *form*, and the light does not fall on this form from above and from outside, rather it breaks forth from the form's interior... The content (*Gehalt*) does not lie outside the form (*Gestalt*) but within it."[35]

Part of the answer for how such beauty is achieved can be found in what may seem like an unlikely place—information theory.

In Chapter 9, we considered that both a repetitious string of letters and a random string of letters contain low information content. A crystalline structure, such as salt, contains a repetitious pattern; and amorphous structures, such as clouds reflecting the light of a sunset, or stellar nebulae, contain random arrangements of particles. All such natural phenomena have low information content. Conversely, the quality of beauty known as inner depth is found in greatest measure in systems with a high information content, in living things.

There is more here to consider. Beauty in nature reveals a conjunction both curious, and curiously fitting. We find depth of beauty in liv-

204 / <small>CANCELED SCIENCE</small> /

ing things; Earth's most intelligent living organisms, humans, alone appear able to intensely appreciate depth of form; and only with intelligent agents do we observe the creation of information-rich artifacts, such as novels and symphonies. Depth of beauty is the purview of the most information-rich structures in nature, living things. Depth of beauty appears to be—in its manifestation, creation, and appreciation—the purview of a mind attuned to beauty.

A living thing's depth of form is coded into its DNA and its other reservoirs of biological information. The form arises from DNA being read in conjunction with the marvelously orchestrated biochemistry of a cell. What is the explanation for such information-rich artistry? One easy response is, "Isn't evolution grand?" Well, something is grand—something or someone. But if we want to address the question of the origin of living forms rationally, merely genuflecting before the theory of evolution won't do. We need to compare the explanatory power of competing explanations and find one with the demonstrated capacity for generating depths of form and information. Blind evolution, I have argued, being subject solely to the laws of nature, lacks that capacity. Intelligent agents, by contrast, have demonstrated this capacity repeatedly.

Human and Animal Designs

ANIMALS, EVEN insects, can create designs that extend beyond the kinds of design produced by the forces of nature alone. Animal designs typically have the added hallmark of functionality—for example, a beehive, or a bird's nest, or a spider's web. However, these designs seem to be pre-programmed or instinctive, and do not originate from the individual creativity of the animal.

Humans, in contrast, can and do create beautiful designs with a seemingly inexhaustible fund of creativity. Humans can endow their designs with functionality or whimsy, can express the complex emotions of the artist, or the mood and outlook of a people or culture at a particular time and place—the zeitgeist.

The fields of painting, sculpture, music, literature, architecture, and engineering all offer proofs in abundance of the human capacity and drive to produce masterful designs. Such work involves matter and a mastery of material forces, but it is more than this. Leonardo Da Vinci said, "The painter has it first in his mind, and then in his hands."[36] Human-level designs far exceed anything the laws of physics and chemistry alone could produce. Nowhere do we find such laws producing, from scratch, anything approaching the Taj Mahal, or a racing yacht, or the space shuttle, or da Vinci's Mona Lisa.

Where we find the greatest depths of form in nature are in forms produced through biological reproduction—life begetting life. And where we directly witness the creation of a form that is fundamentally new, information rich, and of great depth, there is always behind it an intelligent agent—an artist or poet, an architect or engineer. Based on this uniform and repeated experience, biological designs—themselves novel, information rich, and of great depth—would appear to be the prerogative of creative intelligence.

One might argue that nature must at some time have produced living forms in such abundance since, after all, they are all around us. However, that misses the point. Nature's inability to form complex, functional designs is a hard-wired consequence of the laws of physics. We need to make sense both of this and of the fact that life exists in great variety and abundance on planet Earth. A cause beyond that of blind natural forces appears to be called for in order to resolve the tension here.

Beauty Unexpected

PHILOSOPHER RICHARD Swinburne states, "If God creates a universe, as a good workman he will create a beautiful universe. On the other hand, if the universe came into existence without being created by God, there is no reason to suppose that it would be a beautiful universe."[37] The presence of beauty in nature, in other words, fits better with theism than with naturalism. Notice that line of thinking is not vitiated by the presence of ugliness in nature. Swinburne's point is that in a happenstance universe, we should not expect any sort of beauty. And yet we find a great deal of it.

But Swinburne's argument does raise some questions. If nature is the work of a wise divine designer, why is there any ugliness in nature, any pain, any brokenness? To such worthwhile theological questions there are good theological answers,[38] but answers that would take us far beyond this book's scope. A related question is, If the designer is all-wise, why would he have to interfere to make "corrections" later? Some say that if God created the universe to operate according to laws of nature, then he would never break those laws by interfering with nature, and therefore miracles would be impossible. But why accept this claim? The laws of nature are regularities in the operation of nature. If a transcendent intelligence wants to set up the universe according to a well-orchestrated set of regularities, and then temporarily suspend some of those regularities to accomplish this or that end not achievable strictly through those regularities, who is to say this is bad form?

It certainly doesn't violate any widely accepted aesthetic rule in the arts. Take as a parallel case, the regularities in an artful poem—its rhyme and meter. An exception to a poem's rhyme or meter could be ugly and ill-advised, but it could also be artful, making for a better poem than if the poet had stuck rigidly to the poem's rhyme scheme or metrical rhythm. No poet or poetry teacher worth her salt would insist that all such exceptions are necessarily bad. One would have to dump Shakespeare[39] and many other great poets into the dustbin if one stuck to such an insistence.

A miracle, moreover, need not destroy the natural order, but could instead merge smoothly into it. Humans are constantly causing things to happen that would never happen naturally. And if humans can bring about events beyond the reach of natural laws, why couldn't the maker of the natural order? In the words of C. S. Lewis, "We see every day that physical nature is not in the least incommoded by the daily inrush of events from biological nature or from psychological nature. If events ever come from beyond Nature altogether, she will be no more incommoded by them."[40]

Summary and Reflection

ONE MAY get the impression from certain scientists that it's inherently more rational, more scientific, to treat the mind as a mere epiphenomenon of brain chemistry, and then to dismiss as a mirage the experience of being transported by beauty, of sensing that there is something more to reality than the physical, something transcendent. But in fact such a reflexive dismissal isn't rational. It's blindly dogmatic. Moreover, the argument for naturalism attacks the basis for trusting in rationality, sawing off the very limb the philosophical naturalist sits on while making an argument that material nature is all there is.

As for our experience of beauty, the more we reflect on it and on the nature of beauty, the more connections we find with intelligence and creativity, with the generation of form and information, most especially as we contemplate radiant beauty. Perhaps, then, those moments when we are pierced by great beauty, and by an attendant sense that there is something here that transcends the material, are not illusions but evidence.

12. "What a Work"

The famous American physicist John Wheeler did not shy away from seeking to understand the most fundamental aspects of our universe. Wheeler coined the aphorism "It from bit" to describe his conviction, born of the many discoveries in particle physics and cosmology in the twentieth century, that information (characterized by the computer storage term "bit") preceded and produced everything else ("it"). He elaborated:

> Otherwise put, every it—every particle, every field of force, even the space-time continuum itself—derives its function, its meaning, its very existence entirely—even if in some contexts indirectly—from the apparatus-elicited answers to yes or no questions, binary choices, bits.
>
> It from Bit symbolizes the idea that every item of the physical world has at bottom—at a very deep bottom, in most instances—an immaterial source and explanation; that what we call reality arises in the last analysis from the posing of yes-no questions and the registering of equipment-evoked responses; in short, that all things physical are information-theoretic in origin.[1]

Thus, in Wheeler's conception, information precedes and transcends matter, energy, time, and space.

We also know, as philosopher of science Stephen Meyer has emphasized, that in every case where we are able to trace information back to a source, we arrive at an intelligent agent—a poet or computer programmer or composer or architect.[2] When we couple the "It from Bit" insight with this observation regarding our uniform experience with information creation, we are led toward a conclusion that strongly echoes a core claim of theistic religion such as we find in the Hebrew scriptures announcing that nature "pours forth speech" and is the result of a divine mind's spoken words "in the beginning"[3]—or, as one of the New Testament authors put it, "In the beginning was the Word, and the Word was with God, and the Word was God," and "all things were made through him."[4]

Quantum physicist Anton Zeilinger, in reviewing Wheeler's contributions to quantum phenomena, notes this same connection between the discoveries of modern physics and what he terms "old knowledge." Zeilinger states:

> In conclusion it may very well be said that information is the irreducible kernel from which everything else flows. Then the question why nature appears quantized is simply a consequence of the fact that information itself is quantized by necessity. It might even be fair to observe that the concept that information is fundamental is very old knowledge of humanity, witness for example the beginning of gospel according to John: 'In the beginning was the Word.'[5]

While we can marvel at the discovery of how information-dependent our universe is down to its elementary foundations, we also are justified in raising an eyebrow at the dramatic jump in the information content of the universe upon the arrival of the first living thing.

A well-established fact is that the universe at one time contained no biological life of any kind. We know this because the physical conditions that prevailed before the formation of stars and planets made biological life impossible. But then at some point after the conditions were right, life appeared. This was a major change, to say the least.

If we plot the information content of the universe as a function of time, it gradually decreased from the moment of its beginning. The initial, fairly uniform distribution of matter and energy (uniform to one part in 100,000) began to contract under the force of gravity into larger structures that became galaxies containing stars. Yes, entropy increases and information decreases in the process of the gravitational collapse of a large gas cloud into a galactic or stellar system.[6] But then, a living single-celled organism appeared for the first time in the universe, and the information content of the universe suddenly and dramatically increased.[7]

As noted in Chapter 9, this event was in direct opposition to the generalized second law of thermodynamics. If this generalized second law is any indication, this transition of the universe from a state devoid of life to a state containing life stands out as something beyond the reach of both chance and law-like processes.

The laws of physics, delineated by painstaking observation, support a general physical principle that limits the natural production of information to a level far below what is needed for the simplest form of life. In this case it becomes futile to speculate about various naturalistic origin-of-life scenarios, such as RNA first,[8] proteins first, self-organization, deep-sea thermal vents, or a subterranean origin of life. All possible natural scenarios fail because nature cannot overcome the gargantuan information barrier between non-life and life.

Research scientist Robert Gange illustrated the comprehensive inability of nature to generate more information than the universe originally contained:

> The New Generalized Second Law... tells us that natural machinery does not exist to *systematically* increase the complexity of biological structures with the passage of time.... It is the basic result that regulates physical matter. This indicates that regardless of what we might conjecture to be the alleged "natural" explanation for the progression of increased complexity... it will be untrue in the same way a patent examiner in Washington, D.C. knows an alleged invention for a perpetual motion machine is untrue.[9]

In other words, the patent examiner who receives a patent application for a perpetual motion machine "based on revolutionary new technology" does not need to even investigate the mechanism before stamping it *rejected*. The well-established second law of thermodynamics summarily precludes any such device from working, no matter what its internal mechanism might be. So it is, I would suggest, with any imagined natural mechanism that purports to ratchet up information content beyond what the system previously contained.

Beyond Primitive Religion

PRESCIENTIFIC PEOPLES used to worship rocks or carved pieces of wood and declare, "My father!" But that practice became unfashionable well before the age of science. So then, it was thought that the Earth gave birth to life (exchanging a small rock for a large one). But scientists began to realize that even this was unlikely, so an appeal was made to the greater universe for the origin of life.[10] With the advent of further understanding of the vast information content of biomolecules and the low probability of any sort of chance assemblage of such molecules within our universe, the size of the "father rock" was enormously expanded to encompass multiple universes. We could be excused for wondering, Are not all such explanations fraught with the same essential absurdity—calling a rock "My father"?

Perhaps we unconsciously ascribe fertility to the Earth, since out of its soil grow all of the plants that provide food for animals and for us. And yet the Earth would produce nothing without the seeds of the plants. One of biology's "universal laws" (accredited to Rudolph Virchow) states, "Every cell comes from a preexistent cell."[11] So we look to the seed, and what do we find? A rich storehouse of information coded in the seed's DNA. We find information as the source of the physical complexity of life; the Earth is just the environment in which the seed's hidden information can be unfolded and activated.

From where does the information embedded within the seed come? Not from the Earth, nor from the stars, nor from the Big Bang origin of the physical universe. One possibility—one that some refuse even to consider—is that the information found in a seed ultimately comes from a mind. A maker. And based strictly on the unmatched sophistication of these information systems, a mind far above ours.

There is good news here. Nature itself testifies that our lives may indeed have more significance than could be found in a merely naturalistic universe. The question for each of us, and our scientific culture generally, is whether we are willing even to consider this testimony. For some the answer is an authoritative, and indeed, authoritarian *no*.

Silencing the Evidence

IT'S ONE thing to make observations of nature and match theories to experimental results. It's quite another thing to mandate that the study of nature only be done while holding onto a particular interpretation of nature—naturalism. Those who make this demand strive to silence any consideration of nature that looks beyond the limits of naturalistic science. These activists often justify their censorship by claiming that they are protecting students in public schools or society in general from government-sponsored religion. But in reality they are trying to forcibly instill their own religion by spreading the unsubstantiated belief that nothing exists beyond the realm of nature.

Such activists have done a good job of inculcating the view that opposition to their dogmatic position is taboo in academic settings. During the years I taught the Boundaries of Science course, occasionally a student would complain that a book he or she chose to review for a course assignment was "one-sided" in presenting evidence for intelligent design. What such students overlooked was that many of the books they might have chosen to review were one-sided in the other direction. And indeed, most contemporary origins science books—and most science courses dealing with origins—are one-sided in favor of a purely naturalistic viewpoint of origins.

By examining nature we have seen that there is a limit to what nature can accomplish, and that there is a reasonable case to be made that that limit falls short of being able to generate the universe as a whole, its finely tuned laws and constants, the specific conditions of planet Earth, the development of life on Earth, and the advent of consciousness and the human mind. To sweep this evidence aside and insist that natural explanations are sufficient to explain everything "because of science" is to go beyond the reach of science and into philosophical dogma.

When confronted with something that falls outside our familiar models or worldview, an all-too-human inclination is to reject the reality of the thing. Our preconceptions can be stubbornly resistant to change, and history shows that even educated, intelligent people can tragically reject the truth of something that threatens their worldview. A key attribute to gaining truth is the humility to remain open to new evidence.

So then, what if science has found that the evidence from nature poorly aligns with naturalism and aligns well with theism? To exclude such a conclusion by asserting that "it isn't science" should be taken for what it is, the sort of courtroom tactic one uses when evidence is lacking. In scientific education, the *modus operandi* should be to proceed with an open mind and open dialogue regarding all the evidence available. The goal of true education is not to force a propagandized rhetoric intolerant of dissenting views.

In university teaching, refraining from dogmatic insistence upon one's own interpretation of the evidence promotes civility and encourages students to develop critical thinking skills. It should go without saying that professors should treat students of all beliefs and backgrounds with tolerance and respect. Humility and kindness, even when convictions are strong, is more becoming than arrogance. Professors should treat fellow professors who hold differing viewpoints with respect as well—this is a hallmark of academic freedom. I am fortunate to have known many such professors in my academic career, both at Ball State and elsewhere.

There is room for atheists, agnostics, pantheists, deists, and theists in the scientific enterprise. But I would submit that the one who allows for the possibility of causes beyond randomness and materialism is freer to follow the evidence wherever it may lead. She sees herself as the humble admirer learning the secrets of the divine craftsman, whether those secrets involve finely tuned regularities such as we find in the mathematically tractable laws of physics, or discreet acts of creation, such as the creation of the universe out of nothing in the moment of the Big Bang.

This openness is not the dramatic detour from accepted scientific practice that it may at first seem. The conviction that nature was the rational work of a divine craftsman was the view of the founders of modern science, including Copernicus, Kepler, and Newton. And there are many distinguished modern scientists who take such a view. Rosalind Picard, founder and director of the Affective Computing Research Group at the Massachusetts Institute of Technology, is quite pointed on the matter. "I once thought I was too smart to believe in God," she said. "Now I know I was an arrogant fool who snubbed the greatest Mind in the cosmos— the Author of all science, mathematics, art, and everything else there is to know. Today I walk humbly, having received the most undeserved grace. I walk with joy, alongside the most amazing Companion anyone could ask for, filled with desire to keep learning and exploring."[12]

Academic Freedom vs. Academic Integrity

EARLY IN my teaching career, in order to engage students in my introductory astronomy courses in the process of learning, I often started off the semester by asking some open-ended questions, such as those touched upon in Chapter 1. Some of these questions, and students' responses, would become class discussion topics later in the term, and so over the course of several years, from reading hundreds and hundreds of student responses, I gained a fair amount of insight into what college students think about these topics.

Some of the most poignant responses came from the questions they would most like answered. The most common questions usually revolved around the existence of God, or the meaning of their existence, or life after death. Other responses had to do with how best to make their lives count for something worthwhile. These responses showed me that many students are actually concerned about ultimate questions, more than the popular stereotype of college students might lead some people to think.

Even a brief time spent giving feedback to the class about their responses to these questions aided in building a bridge across the usual professor-student divide. After a few years of analyzing responses to these questions in a number of introductory astronomy classes, I wrote a short article called "Questions from the Edge" for the *Journal of College*

Science Teaching, published by the National Science Teachers Association.[13] The article sorted responses from students into various categories and discussed how science teachers could beneficially engage students in class through asking similar questions to connect with student interests at a deeper level.

Was there anything academically improper about this approach? As stated earlier, academic freedom has extensive legal protection in the United States and includes the right to teach viewpoints that are unpopular, unproven, or controversial. Its companion, academic integrity, involves an appeal to common sense: if a professor is being paid to teach mathematics, he or she cannot rightfully spend the class period teaching English literature. So, what if a science professor discusses well-established scientific evidence that potentially undermines the presupposition of naturalism? What if this is done in a course that is expected to discuss the intersection of science and society? And what if many scientific academies have politically motivated statements labeling the connection between such topics as unscientific? Do we therefore censor the discussion of the evidence within the context of a university science class? I submit that it is a questionable application of the principle of academic integrity to forbid discussions of on-topic scientific evidence whose implications do not agree with atheism, or any other particular worldview.

William W. Van Alstyne notes that the American Association of University Professors (AAUP) has long expressed a similar view towards teaching: "As Arthur Lovejoy (a founder of the AAUP in 1913) observed in the 1930 edition of the *Encyclopaedia of the Social Sciences*, the ultimate social good of a university 'is rendered impossible if the work of the investigator is shackled by the requirement that his conclusions shall never seriously deviate from generally accepted beliefs.'"[14]

Today there's a critical need to interest more students in studying the fundamental sciences. It is my experience, informed by what students themselves have written, that discussing relevant implications of various scientific theories and discoveries fuels student interest in the study of these fields.

So, too, does allowing room for critical thinking and debate about unresolved issues such as how life first arose, or what the source of nature's finely tuned laws for life is. Students need to be given room for discussion and allowed to form their own conclusions regarding an idea's validity. Doing so also can make for a more compelling classroom experience. Indeed, when discussing the implications of scientific theories and scientific evidence in class, the discussions can get pretty lively at times as students present various viewpoints. Professors may be tempted to avoid this by steering away from controversial topics and minimizing discussion and debate, but this approach exacts its own cost. As astronomer Hugh Ross put it, "The price of not allowing debate in science is to make science boring."[15]

A significant study was conducted by professors from the Higher Education Research Institute at UCLA from 2003–2007, during which more than 112,000 students were surveyed. The focus and the published results of this comprehensive survey support the thesis that discussing ultimate questions in the context of a college education provides a valuable and needed connection with students.

"Our primary reason for undertaking this study has been our shared belief that *spirituality is fundamental to students' lives*," the authors of the UCLA study write. "The 'big questions' that preoccupy students are essentially spiritual questions: Who am I? What are my most deeply felt values? Do I have a mission or purpose in my life? Why am I in college? What kind of person do I want to become? What sort of world do I want to help create?"[16]

I can personally testify to this conclusion. After teaching in the physics and astronomy department at Ball State University for a few years, I had developed a relationship with a number of the students. One of them had recently become a Christian, another was a Mormon, a couple of them were atheists, others had a church background growing up, and with some of them, I didn't know what their outlook or particular upbringing was. We began to meet together for a "faith and science discussion group" one evening a week at my house. My wife would fix brownies and other snacks, and we'd share thoughts on questions they found interesting.

On one of the first evenings, a student came who obviously felt uncomfortable. He was a big guy with tattoos, piercings, and chains. We had welcomed him in to our living room, but he stood there almost frozen until my five-year-old daughter came up and took his hand to add her welcome. The picture of his big hand, with his fingernails all painted black, contrasted with my daughter's little girl hand, still impacts me. He eventually relaxed, realizing that he really was welcome, and became a regular. Over the months the group met, I don't know if anybody ended up changing their beliefs, but they all enjoyed the sense of acceptance. And everyone appreciated the chance to explore some questions focused around the overlap of faith and science.

Seeking the answers to such questions defines what the authors of the UCLA study term the "spiritual quest" of students. The authors warn of the dangers of excising such an inquiry from the academic experience:

> To ignore the spiritual side of students' and faculty's lives is to encourage a kind of fragmentation and a lack of authenticity, where students and faculty act either as if they are not spiritual beings, or as if their spiritual side is irrelevant to their vocation or work. Within such an environment, academic endeavors can become separated from students' most deeply felt values, and students may hesitate to discuss issues of meaning, purpose, authenticity, and wholeness with each other and especially with faculty. This kind of fragmentation is further encouraged by those who believe that higher education should concern itself only with students' "cognitive" development—thinking, reasoning, memorizing, critical analysis, and the like—and that the affective or emotional side of the student's life is not relevant to the work of the university.[17]

The cost of disconnecting academic learning and development from the spiritual aspect of human nature exacts a high price. Distinguished cell biologist Franklin Harold wrote, "It is not at all self-evident that, absent a belief in powers greater than ourselves, a decent and civilized society can be sustained for long."[18]

To conclude that these powers are nothing other than the forces of nature not only clashes with scientific and philosophical evidence, it fails to provide any basis for either hope or rationality.

And while the details of life's significance and purpose are appropriately left to religion, philosophy, and the arts, the pervasive human attraction to the divine, and the hope in the possibility of eternal life, is nevertheless found to be consistent with what we can glean from the scientific study of this universe.

Indeed, the reality uncovered by scientific inquiry strongly suggests that physical reality is embedded within a higher, transcendent reality from which originates the design of our universe's laws, the form and information essential to living things, along with consciousness and our immaterial minds.

Some prefer to look for purely material explanations—nature explaining nature, all the way to a hypothetically infinite past. But as I have made an effort to show, everything we know about nature tells us that it has a finite lifespan; it had a beginning, and it will have an end. So, to suggest that nature itself, even in the guise of an extra-dimensional multiverse, is its own ultimate cause is inconsistent with logic and scientific understanding.

What of the alternative—the God of the philosophers, a transcendent maker of the cosmos who is immaterial, transcendent, and has neither beginning nor end? Such a being meets the requirements for an ultimate cause of the physical universe. Such a being is, in turn, consistent with the God of various religions and philosophical outlooks, including Judaism, Islam, Christianity, and what we might call rational theism. At the same time, it remains a conclusion reached by logical reasoning and one fully consistent with our scientific understanding of the universe. This inference to a cosmic designer involves evidence about the beginning of the cosmos alongside evidence of intelligent design in physics, chemistry, and biology. It includes careful reasoning about what nature can and cannot accomplish, about what mindless forces can and cannot do, and about what activities appear to be the exclusive domain of mind.

Walking through Persecution

I BEGAN this book by describing the assault launched against my Boundaries of Science course at Ball State University, an assault spearheaded by atheists from outside the university and the state. I survived the assault but my course did not. It was a rough ride that I wouldn't wish on anyone, but blessings have come as a result of the public nature of the attacks. I've been able to get to know people from all over the country who heard of what happened to me and reached out to share encouragement and support. I was never alone through this experience. Many people expressed that they were praying for my family and me, and I can't imagine having gone through it without this source of support.

Early on, after the first media articles had come out, I received a call from one of the researchers at the Discovery Institute's Center for Science and Culture in Seattle. The center's mission is to advance the scientific evidence for intelligent design and the freedom to follow the evidence in origins science wherever it leads. They saw my Boundaries of Science course as a model for encouraging university students to freely explore the evidence pro and con.[19] Their team had helped to defend other scientists who had also come under attack from anti-design activists, and I also greatly benefited from their friendship and support. The people at Discovery Institute provided much helpful behind-the-scenes advice and advocacy. They also wrote accurate media responses to the misleading caricatures of my course that other media sources circulated from uninformed sources. At Ball State, I was granted the title of associate professor in 2014 and granted tenure two years later. The media seemed to find this incredible, and it sparked recycled misreporting about the controversy over my Boundaries of Science course, misreporting that Discovery Institute again helped to set straight.[20]

As for the university itself, in detailing the attacks on my academic freedom from Jerry Coyne and The Freedom From Religion Foundation, I don't want to let the positive get overshadowed. During my time at Ball State I enjoyed the friendship and support of many fine colleagues. I eventually accepted a position as professor and department chair at a university in California, but I carry with me years of good memories from my time at Ball State.

Another significant source of support during the attacks on my Boundaries course came from pastor and church leader Rice Broocks. I didn't know him at the time, but he has since become well-known for writing the book *God's Not Dead*,[21] which inspired the movie of the same title. In one of our conversations, he suggested that I write a book about my Boundaries of Science course. I had been thinking of doing this for quite some time, but his encouragement motivated me to put words to the page.

Shortly after the atheist attacks on my course began and the media's sensationalized reporting picked up, I also received three separate offers of pro bono legal counsel and representation by constitutional rights organizations. I agreed to have one of these organizations take my case, and what a support they were. It was never my intention to file suit during the attack and Ball State's investigation, since the future of my course—but not my job—was on the line at that time. I was personally treated cordially and with respect by Ball State's administration, and apart from canceling the course and abridging academic freedom concerning discussions of intelligent design, the case was closed by the fall of 2013. I am aware that I can't take this for granted, and tragically, professors at other universities have lost their jobs in situations very similar to what I was going through.

The Wonder of Life

THE ATTACK on my academic freedom was no picnic for me or my family, but still it was not the hardest thing I've ever endured. Most of us who have lived long enough could point to greater hardships. In my life, one of the earlier tests of my faith came when my mother was killed in a car accident just three weeks before the start of my senior year of college.

On the night it happened, I was driving home with my younger sister from a concert in Seattle, and on the way, we both wondered why we felt so miserable and depressed. When reached the house, I remember being surprised at seeing so many cars in our driveway, and I thought my parents must be hosting a party. But as we were getting out of the car, a man who had been my high school youth group leader met us and told us that our mom had been killed. As we walked up to the front door, what struck me so profoundly and unexpectedly was that I felt carried, held up by an inner strength not my own. As we came into the house, my dad met us, and he began to cry as we embraced.

Other experiences subsequent to this event have tried my faith in different ways. Could anything be harder than losing one's mother? Alas, yes. At one point, later in my life, I remember thinking that compared to what I was going through at that time, the grief over my mom's sudden death felt almost sweet. There were times when all I felt I could do was to keep breathing. Yet, even from such a desperate situation, restoration has come.

The figure of Job, the premier example of human suffering as described in the Hebrew Bible, was restored to blessings beyond what he had ever known. But the deeper work was forged within his heart when the hammer blows hit the hardest, giving true power to his words, "I know that my Redeemer lives."[22] I am no Job, but I too have this conviction of faith. I've often said that my strongest assurances of faith come from evidence that could best be described as spiritual. But the discoveries in physics, astronomy, and biochemistry over the past several decades that point to design and the significance of our lives have only strengthened that conviction.

At the center of that evidence is an astronomical body that atheist astronomer Carl Sagan famously described as a "pale blue dot" in the immensity of interstellar space. He meant to emphasize how insignificant it is. But imagine a hypothetical observer of our universe scanning star after star and multitudes of lifeless planets, and then finally coming to Earth. Earth, abounding with life of mind-boggling variety, each living thing unequaled in countless light-years of empty space. The observer would undoubtedly record each living thing as a wonder far surpassing the inter-galactic sameness we see throughout the universe.

As recounted earlier in this book, the origin of the stunning complexity of the biochemical metropolis within each of our trillions of cells cannot be explained by reference alone to natural causes within the space-time boundaries of our universe. When we move from cells to organisms, and from organisms to creatures, the wonders merely increase. And when we move, finally, from primitive creatures to humans, we are right to say with Shakespeare, "What a work is man!"

I vividly remember when my daughter was born, being amazed at how perfect this little person was. To think that she was essentially made from the food my wife ate during the nine months of her pregnancy adds to the wonder of seeing a newborn baby. Imagine the marvel of the human body, which can take the basic ingredients of whatever we eat and convert it into a human child. But the most powerful thing about seeing my newborn daughter was looking into her eyes. There was somebody there looking back at me. Immediately after she was born, this tiny baby connected with me, spirit to spirit. There was no mistaking that she was a person fully alive, complete with personality, will, and emotions.

One reason why some people may prefer naturalism is that they don't really believe that the tenets of naturalism apply to them personally. Holding themselves apart from nature elevates them above nature. Lacking a belief in God, such a person unconsciously begins to regard himself as a little god. The alternative for the atheist is to face the full consequences of his naturalism and thereby fall into a meaningless existence, one where he regards himself as merely a pile of atoms governed by natural law, without moral responsibility, free will, and the capacity for genuine love, honor, or courage—a machine made of meat, and nothing more.

The good news is that the scientific evidence actually testifies that we are much more than just a pile of atoms, that reality is more than matter in motion, and that our existence is consistent with intention and design. The old conviction remains eminently plausible: we are free beings created by the free choice of a master artist, with inherent significance and purpose.

ENDNOTES

1. THE BOUNDARIES OF SCIENCE (9–36)

1. Rodney D. Holder, *God, the Multiverse, and Everything: Modern Cosmology and the Argument from Design* (Aldershot and Burlington, VT: Ashgate Publishing, 2004), 2.

2. Franklin M. Harold, *The Way of the Cell* (Oxford: Oxford University Press, 2001), 255.

3. *Scientific American* 285, no. 4 (October 2001), https://www.scientificamerican.com/magazine/sa/2001/10-01/.

4. Jerry Coyne, "'Science' Course at Ball State University Sneaks in Religion," Why Evolution Is True, April 25, 3013, https://whyevolutionistrue.com/2013/04/25/science-course-at-ball-state-university-sneaks-in-religion/.

5. David Klinghoffer, "At Ball State University, Intimidation Campaign Against Physicist Gets Troubling Results," Evolution News and Views, Discovery Institute, May 22, 2013, https://evolutionnews.org/2013/05/at_ball_state_u/. Laurence Moran, "Inside Higher Ed Weighs in on the Ball State Academic Freedom Controversy," Sandwalk, May 17, 2013, https://sandwalk.blogspot.com/2013/05/inside-higher-ed-weighs-in-on-ball.html.

6. John G. West, "Misrepresenting the Facts about Eric Hedin's 'Reading List,'" Evolution News and Views, Discovery Institute, July 11, 2013, https://evolutionnews.org/2013/07/misrepresenting/.

7. Victor Stenger, "Does Academic Freedom Give Professors the Right to Teach Whatever They Want?," Huffington Post, May 25, 2013, https://www.huffpost.com/entry/teach-does-academic-freed_b_3335371.

8. Ball State *University Faculty and Professional Personnel Handbook* 2012–2013, 64.

9. Malachi W. Randolph, quoted in David Klinghoffer, "An Undergraduate Student Writes: Ball State University Student Body President Speaks Out, But Is the University Listening?" Evolution News and Views, Discovery Institute, July 12, 2013, https://evolutionnews.org/2013/07/ball_state_univ/.

10. Peter Schmidt, "Ball State U. Bars Teaching of Intelligent Design as Science," *Chronicle of Higher Education*, August 1, 2013, https://www.chronicle.com/article/ball-state-u-bars-teaching-of-intelligent-design-as-science.

11. John G. West, "Questions Raised about Impartiality of Panel Reviewing Ball State University Professor's Course," Evolution News and Views, Discovery Institute, June 25, 2013, https://evolutionnews.org/2013/06/review_panel_or/.

12. John G. West, "A Tale of Two Professors," Evolution News and Views, Discovery Institute, June 26, 2013, https://evolutionnews.org/2013/06/a_tale_of_two_p/.

13. State Senator Dennis K. Kruse, State Senator Travis Holdman, State Senator Greg Walker, and State Representative Jeffrey Thompson to Ball State University President Jo Ann Gora and the Ball State Board of Trustees, March 10, 2014, https://www.discovery.org/m/2014/03/IN-Leg-Ltr-BSU.pdf.

14. Quoted in Joshua Youngkin, "Dr. Hedin's Student Could Teach Ball State University a Thing or Two," Evolution News and Views, Discovery Institute, July 16, 2013, https://evolutionnews.org/2013/07/what_happened_i/.

15. Quoted in Youngkin, "Dr. Hedin's Student."

16. Leigh Smith, online comment on Seth Slabaugh, "Ball State Prof Accused of Preaching Christianity," Star Press, May 21, 2013, A1.

17. John West, quoted in "Ball State University President Imposes Gag Order on Scientists Supportive of Intelligent Design," Evolution News and Views, Discovery Institute, July 31, 2013, https://evolutionnews.org/2013/07/ball_state_univ_1/.

18. Casey Luskin, "False Spin: Ball State University Misrepresents Anti-Religious Chapters in What Is Your Dangerous Idea? as Religion-Friendly," Evolution News and Views, Discovery Institute, March 17, 2014, https://evolutionnews.org/2014/03/false_spin_ball/.

19. Antony Flew, There is a God (San Francisco: HarperOne, 2008), 91.

20. Flew, There is a God, 91.

2. ROOTED IN REALITY (37–50)

1. Krister Renard, Vetenskap och Tro: Två Vägar till en Världsbild (Örebro, Sverige: Libris, 1989), 162.

2. Thomas Dubay, S. M., The Evidential Power of Beauty: Science and Theology Meet (San Francisco: Ignatius Press, 1999), 61.

3. Douglas Axe, Undeniable: How Biology Confirms Our Intuition That Life Is Designed (New York: Harper One, 2016).

4. The saying is variously attributed, and in various forms. The earliest occurrence I could confirm was by British geneticist J. B. S. Haldane, "Possible Worlds," Possible Worlds and Other Papers [1927] (New York: Routledge, 2002), 286.

3. THE COSMIC QUEST (51–62)

1. Jeffrey Bennett et al., The Cosmic Perspective: The Solar System, 7th ed. (San Francisco: Pearson, 2014), 71.

2. Geraint F. Lewis and Luke A. Barnes, A Fortunate Universe: Life in a Finely Tuned Cosmos (Cambridge, UK: Cambridge University Press, 2016), 196.

3. Robin Collins, "The Fine-Tuning Design Argument," in Reason for the Hope Within, ed. Michael Murray (Grand Rapids, MI: Eerdmans, 1999), 47–75.

4. Infinite regresses in time are a problem because there doesn't appear to be a way to ever reach the present if the universe has existed for an infinitely long time into the past. How would you ever reach the present if you had to transverse an infinite amount of time to get here?

5. Michael A. Seeds and Dana E. Backman, Astronomy: The Solar System and Beyond, 6th ed. (Belmont, CA: Brooks Cole Publishing, 2010), 438–439.

6. Bennett et al., The Cosmic Perspective (2014), 419–420.

7. Since the speed at which galaxies move apart due to the expansion of space is proportional to the distance between them, local motions of galaxies can modify or even reverse this effect. For example, within our local group of galaxies, the Andromeda galaxy (only about 2.4 million light years away) is moving towards our galaxy, the Milky Way. However, for

more distant galaxies (billions of light years away), the expansion of space becomes the dominant factor, leading to the general trend described by Hubble's Law.

8. "Planck Reveals an Almost Perfect Universe," European Space Agency, March 21, 2013, http://www.esa.int/Our_Activities/Space_Science/Planck/Planck_reveals_an_almost_perfect_Universe.

9. Stephen Hawking and Roger Penrose, "The Singularities of Gravitational Collapse and Cosmology," *Proceedings of the Royal Society of London* A 314 (January 27, 1970): 529–548.

10. Stephen Hawking, *A Brief History of Time*, (London: Bantam Press, 1988); Stephen Hawking and Leonard Mlodinow. *The Grand Design: New Answers to the Ultimate Questions of Life* (London: Bantam Press, 2010).

11. Eric R. Hedin, "The Cosmological Singularity," *Dictionary of Christianity and Science: The Definitive Reference for the Intersection of Christian Faith and Contemporary Science*, P. Copan, T. Longman III, C. L. Reese, and M. G. Strauss, eds. (Grand Rapids, MI: Zondervan, 2017), 115.

12. Brian Greene, *The Fabric of the Cosmos* (New York: Vintage Books, 2004), 174–175.

4. ON A KNIFE EDGE (63–78)

1. Geraint F. Lewis and Luke A. Barnes, *A Fortunate Universe: Life in a Finely-Tuned Cosmos* (Cambridge: Cambridge University Press, 2016); John D. Barrow and Frank J. Tipler, *The Anthropic Cosmological Principle* (Oxford: Oxford University Press, 1986); Rodney D. Holder, *God, the Multiverse, and Everything* (Abingdon, UK: Routledge, 2004); Robin Collins, "Evidence for Fine-Tuning," in *God and Design: The Teleological Argument and Modern Science*, ed. Neil A. Manson (Abingdon, UK: Routledge, 2003); Martin Rees, *Just Six Numbers: The Deep Forces That Shape the Universe* (London: Weidenfeld and Nicolson, 1999); Paul Davies, *The Goldilocks Enigma: Why is the Universe Just Right for Life?* (London: Allen Lane, 2006).

2. For discussion of the firing squad illustration in the context of cosmic fine tuning, see John Leslie, *Universes* (London: Routledge, 1989), 13–15, 108.

3. John Leslie, "How to Draw Conclusions from a Fine-Tuned Cosmos," in *Physics, Philosophy and Theology: A Common Quest for Understanding*, eds. Robert Russell et al. (Vatican City State: Vatican Observatory Press, 1988), 297–312.

4. Fred Hoyle, "The Universe: Past and Present Reflections," *Engineering and Science* (November 1981): 12.

5. Lewis and Barnes, *A Fortunate Universe*, 165; Rodney Holder, *Big Bang, Big God: A Universe Designed for Life?* (Oxford: Lion Books, 2013), 88; Hugh Ross, *Why the Universe Is the Way It Is* (Grand Rapids: Baker Books, 2008), 35; Peter Coles, ed., *The Routledge Critical Dictionary of the New Cosmology* (New York: Routledge, 1998); Peter Coles and George F. R. Ellis, *Is the Universe Open or Closed? The Density of Matter in the Universe* (Cambridge: Cambridge University Press, 1997).

6. Holder, *Big Bang, Big God*, 120–23; Barrow and Tipler, *The Anthropic Cosmological Principle*, 435–38.

7. Holder, *Big Bang, Big God*, 136.

8. C. D. McCoy, "Does Inflation Solve the Hot Big Bang Model's Fine-Tuning Problems?," *Studies in History and Philosophy of Modern Physics* 51 (2015): 23–36.

9. Michael A. Seeds and Dana Backman, *Foundations of Astronomy*, 11th ed. (Boston: Brooks Cole, 2010), 419–20.

10. "The Nobel Prize in Physics 2011," http://www.nobelprize.org/nobel_prizes/physics/laureates/2011/press.html.

11. Jeffrey O. Bennett et al., *The Cosmic Perspective*, 7th ed. (London: Pearson, 2014), 490.

12. Davies, *The Goldilocks Enigma*, 149; Holder, *Big Bang, Big God*, 91–92; Lawrence M. Krauss, *Quintessence: The Mystery of the Missing Mass* (New York: Basic, 2000).

13. Roger Penrose, *The Road to Reality: A Complete Guide to the Laws of the Universe* (New York: Alfred A. Knopf, 2004), 726.

14. Bennett et al., *The Cosmic Perspective* (2014), 477.

15. Ralph A. Alpher and Robert Herman, "Reflections on Early Work on 'Big Bang' Cosmology," *Physics Today* 41 (1988): 24–34, doi: 10.1063/1.881126.

16. Seeds and Backman, *Foundations of Astronomy*, 410.

17. Bennett et al., *The Cosmic Perspective* (2014), 481.

18. Seeds and Backman, *Foundations of Astronomy*, 424.

19. Bennett et al., *The Cosmic Perspective* (2014), 490.

20. Bennett et al., *The Cosmic Perspective* (2014), 456.

21. Since direct observational evidence for dark matter has not yet been obtained, some scientists have proposed an alternative explanation for the unexpected stellar velocities in galaxies. This explanation suggests that Newton's law of gravity takes on a different form in which the gravitational force falls off as one over the distance between masses, instead of one over the distance squared. This modification would result in the observed dynamics of the orbital velocities of stars over galactic distances, but would not be noticeable on smaller distance scales, where Newton's familiar force of gravity is observed (R. H. Sanders and S. S. McGaugh, "Modified Newtonian Dynamics as an Alternative to Dark Matter," *Annual Review of Astronomy and Astrophysics* 40 (2002): 263–317, arXiv:astro-ph/0204521v1). The common name for theories invoking a modification of Newton's law of gravity is "modified Newtonian dynamics" (MOND). While such theories could explain stellar orbital velocities without the need for dark matter, MOND theories have not been as successful in explaining other effects attributed to the contribution of dark matter, such as gravitational lensing by galaxy clusters (Jeffrey Bennett et al., *The Cosmic Perspective*, 8th ed. (San Francisco: Pearson, 2017), 676). Gravitational wave detection from the coalescence of neutron stars also has provided observational evidence that falsifies a class of modified gravity theories (Sibel Boran et al., "GW170817 Falsifies Dark Matter Emulators," *Physical Review D* (February 13, 2018): 041501-041505). Notice, however, that regardless of what's eventually discovered vis à vis dark matter and dark energy, the fine tuning would remain, and would merely play out in a different model than the dark matter and dark energy models currently in ascendance.

22. Measurements of the ratio of deuterium (heavy hydrogen) to hydrogen in the universe place a limit on the amount of normal (non-dark) matter in the universe, showing that normal matter can only be about 5% of the critical density needed to produce the observed geometrical flatness of space. Dark matter is estimated to comprise about 25% of the critical density, with most of the rest being contributed by dark energy. Bennett et al., *The Cosmic Perspective* (2014), 678–679.

23. R. Cerulli et al., "DAMA Annual Modulation and Mirror Dark Matter," *The European Physical Journal C : Particles and Fields* 77, no. 2 (2017): 1-20; J. J. Chapman et al., "The Large Underground Xenon (LUX) Experiment," *Nuclear Instruments and Methods in Phys-*

ics Research, Section A: Accelerators, Spectrometers, Detectors and Associated Equipment 704 (2013): 111–126.

24. Elizabeth Gibney, "Last Chance for Wimps: Physicists Launch All-Out Hunt for Dark-Matter Candidate," *Nature* 586, no. 7829 (October 2020): 344–345.

25. E. R. Hedin, "Extradimensional Confinement of Quantum Particles," *Physics Essays* 25 (2012): 2.

26. Neil Comins and William Kaufmann III, *Discovering the Universe,* 10th ed. (New York: W. H. Freeman and Company, 2014), 551.

27. "The Dark Energy Survey," http://www.darkenergysurvey.org/.

28. Comins and Kaufmann, *Discovering the Universe,* 552.

29. Davies, *The Goldilocks Enigma,* 149.

30. Comins and Kaufmann, *Discovering the Universe,* 549.

31. Ross, *Why the Universe is the Way It Is,* 210.

5. VAST AND ANCIENT (79–90)

1. Michael A. Seeds and Dana Backman, *Foundations of Astronomy,* 11th ed. (Boston: Brooks Cole, 2010), 411.

2. Neil Comins and William Kaufmann III, *Discovering the Universe,* 10th ed. (New York: W. H. Freeman and Company, 2014), 544.

3. Seeds and Backman, *Foundations of Astronomy,* 288.

4. Erik Zackrisson et. al, "'Terrestrial Planets Across Space and Time," *The Astrophysical Journal* 833, no. 2 (2016): 214, https://iopscience.iop.org/article/10.3847/1538-4357/833/2/214/pdf. When estimating the required time, a complicating factor is galactic habitable zones, which require a balance between the availability of heavy elements and low enough radiation from nearby stars. The denser regions of a galaxy will accrue metals faster and form large planets earlier, but these regions tend to be much more dangerous for life due to higher levels of stellar radiation.

5. Jonathan Lunine, *Earth: Evolution of a Habitable World,* 2nd ed. (New York: Cambridge University Press, 2013), 167-68; Hugh Ross, *Why the Universe Is the Way It Is* (Grand Rapids: Baker Books, 2008), 45–46.

6. In an interesting development, Stephen Hawking's final research paper indicates that a multiverse containing too many universes is questionable. Hawking and his co-author develop a model that "implies a significant reduction of the multiverse to a much more limited set of possible universes." S. W. Hawking and Thomas Hertog, "A Smooth Exit from Eternal Inflation?," *Journal of High Energy Physics* (2018): 147, arXiv:1707.07702v3 [hep-th].

7. Paul Davies, *The Goldilocks Enigma: Why is the Universe Just Right for Life?* (London: Allen Lane, 2006), 217.

8. Hugh Ross, *The Creator and the Cosmos,* 3rd ed. (Colorado Springs: NavPress, 2011), 153.

9. William Lane Craig and Quentin Smith, *Theism, Atheism, and Big Bang Cosmology* (Oxford: Oxford University Press, 1993).

10. Bruce Gordon, "Balloons on a String: A Critique of Multiverse Cosmology," in *The Nature of Nature: Examining the Role of Naturalism in Science,* eds. Bruce L. Gordon and William A. Dembski (Delaware: ISI Books, 2011), 583.

11. Edward Harrison, "The Natural Selection of Universes Containing Intelligent Life," *Quarterly Journal of the Royal Astronomical Society* 36, no. 3 (1995): 193–203, cited in Rodney Holder, *God, the Multiverse, and Everything* (London: Ashgate, 2004), 62–63.

12. Harrison, cited in Holder, *God, the Multiverse, and Everything*, 63.

13. Gordon, "Balloons on a String," 584.

14. Arno Penzias, "Creation is Supported by All the Data So Far," in *Cosmos, Bios, Theos: Scientists Reflect on Science, God, and the Origins of the Universe, Life, and Homo Sapiens*, eds. Henry Margenau and Roy A. Varghese (Chicago: Open Court Publishing Company, 1991), 83.

15. Psalm 19:1.

16. Psalm 104:24.

6. The Lives of the Stars (91–122)

1. Neil Comins and William Kaufmann III, *Discovering the Universe*, 10th ed. (New York: W. H. Freeman and Company, 2014), 542.

2. Jeffrey O. Bennett et al., *The Cosmic Perspective: The Solar System*, 7th ed. (San Francisco: Pearson, 2014), 400.

3. Geraint F. Lewis and Luke A. Barnes, *A Fortunate Universe: Life in a Finely Tuned Cosmos* (Cambridge: Cambridge University Press, 2016), 110–111.

4. "The Weak Force," Quantum Chromodynamics 101, Fermi National Accelerator Laboratory, accessed December 7, 2020, https://home.fnal.gov/~cheung/rtes/RTESWeb/LQCD_site/pages/weakforce.htm#:~:text=Elements%20like%20plutonium%20and%20uranium,of%20heat%20from%20the%20sun.

5. Comins and Kaufmann, *Discovering the Universe*, 330.

6. Comins and Kaufmann, *Discovering the Universe*, 332; Ashley G. Smart, "Scintillator Yields Glimpse of Elusive Solar Neutrinos," *Physics Today* 67 (November 2014): 12–14. See also the Borexino Collaboration, "Experimental Evidence of Neutrinos Produced in the CNO Fusion Cycle in the Sun," *Nature* 587 (2020): 577–582.

7. Michael A. Seeds and Dana E. Backman, *Astronomy: The Solar System and Beyond*, 6th ed. (Belmont, CA: Brooks/Cole, 2010), 288.

8. Seeds and Backman, *Astronomy*, 294–295.

9. Fred Hoyle, *Religion and the Scientists: Addresses Delivered in the University Church, Cambridge*, ed. Mervin Stockwood (London: SCM Press, 1959). Quoted in Stephen Hawking and Leonard Mlodinow, *The Grand Design* (New York: Bantam Books, 2010), 159.

10. Hawking and Mlodinow, *The Grand Design*, 165.

11. Thomas T. Arny and Stephen E. Schneider, *Explorations: An Introduction to Astronomy*, 8th ed. (New York: McGraw-Hill, 2017), 373.

12. Seeds and Backman, *Astronomy*, 304.

13. Comins and Kaufmann, *Discovering the Universe*, 410.

14. Comins and Kaufmann, *Discovering the Universe*, 410–411.

15. Comins and Kaufmann, *Discovering the Universe*, 412.

16. Comins and Kaufmann, *Discovering the Universe*, 413.

17. Comins and Kaufmann, *Discovering the Universe*, 414.

18. Christian Ott, "Petascale Simulations of Core-Collapse Supernovae" (lecture, American Physical Society meeting, Savannah, GA, April 2014).

19. Jeffrey O. Bennett et al., *The Cosmic Perspective: The Solar System*, 8th ed. (San Francisco: Pearson, 2017), 547.

20. Bennett et al., *The Cosmic Perspective* (2017), 546.

21. Bennett et al., *The Cosmic Perspective* (2014), 351.

22. More recent research on stellar nucleosynthesis indicates that another process by which elements heavier than iron are produced occurs when a nucleus captures neutrons that are produced in abundance during a supernova explosion. Nuclear stability dictates that these captured neutrons will subsequently decay to protons with the release of an electron (and an antineutrino, to conserve lepton number). Approximately half of the heavy element abundances found in nature are thought to be produced in this manner. M. R. Mumpower et al., "The Impact of Individual Nuclear Properties on R-Process Nucleosynthesis," *Progress in Particle and Nuclear Physics* 86 (January 2016): 86–126. Another exotic mechanism that has received recent attention as a source of certain heavy elements, including gold and platinum, is the merger of a binary neutron star system. This energetic event produces a blast of light that has been named a *kilonova*. "Investigation of the Origin of Heavy Elements," *ScienceDaily*, March 12, 2019, https://www.sciencedaily.com/releases/2019/03/190312092516.htm.

23. Guillermo Gonzalez, Donald Brownlee, and Peter Ward, "The Galactic Habitable Zone: Galactic Chemical Evolution," *Icarus* 152 (July 2001): 185–200.

24. Guillermo Gonzalez and Jay W. Richards, *The Privileged Planet: How Our Place in the Cosmos is Designed for Discovery* (Washington, DC: Regnery Publishing, 2004), 166–167.

25. Comins and Kaufmann, *Discovering the Universe*, 420.

26. Eric R. Hedin, "A Higher Dimensional Model of the Nucleon-Nucleon Central Potential," *Frontiers of Physics* 9 (2014): 234–239.

27. Seeds and Backman, *Astronomy*, 319.

28. Seeds and Backman, *Astronomy*, 320–321.

29. Comins and Kaufmann, *Discovering the Universe*, 421–424.

30. Seeds and Backman, *Astronomy*, 325.

31. B. P. Abbott et al., "Observation of Gravitational Waves from a Binary Black Hole Merger," *Physical Review Letters* 116 (2016): 061102; B. P. Abbott et al., "GW150914: The Advanced LIGO Detectors in the Era of First Discoveries," *Physical Review Letters* 116 (2016): 131103.

32. S. W. Hawking, "Black Hole Explosions?," *Nature* 248 (1974): 3031; Bennett et al., *The Cosmic Perspective* (2017), 459.

33. Comins and Kaufmann, *Discovering the Universe*, 447.

34. Comins and Kaufmann, *Discovering the Universe*, 472.

35. Comins and Kaufmann, *Discovering the Universe*, 444–445.

36. Comins and Kaufmann, *Discovering the Universe*, 517–518.

37. Gonzalez and Richards, *The Privileged Planet*.

7. EARTH, DREAM HOME FOR LIFE (123–140)

1. One thing that makes our planet so livable is that it is a planet. Apart from planets, and possibly their moons, no other location in the vast universe could provide long-term support for life. They are a necessary but far from sufficient condition for habitability.

2. Michael A. Seeds and Dana E. Backman, *Astronomy: The Solar System and Beyond*, 6th ed. (Belmont, CA: Brooks/Cole, 2010), 118.

3. Jeffrey O. Bennett et al., *The Cosmic Perspective: The Solar System*, 7th ed. (San Francisco: Pearson, 2014), 164.

4. Neil Comins and William Kaufmann III, *Discovering the Universe*, 10th ed. (New York: W. H. Freeman and Company, 2014), 137.

5. Comins and Kaufmann, *Discovering the Universe*, 153; "Exoplanet Exploration," NASA, accessed December 9, 2020, https://exoplanets.nasa.gov/discovery/exoplanet-catalog/; "Diagrams: Scatter Plot," The Extrasolar Planets Encylopaedia, accessed December 9, 2020, http://exoplanet.eu/diagrams/.

6. Bennett et al., *The Cosmic Perspective* (2014), 442–43.

7. Bennett et al., *The Cosmic Perspective* (2014), 443.

8. Seeds and Backman, *Astronomy*, 261.

9. Bennett et al., *The Cosmic Perspective* (2014), 200.

10. Bennett et al., *The Cosmic Perspective* (2014), 200; Jeffrey O. Bennett et al., *The Cosmic Perspective: The Solar System*, 8th ed. (San Francisco: Pearson, 2017), 607.

11. Stephen E. Schneider and Thomas T. Arny, *Pathways to Astronomy*, 2nd ed. (New York: McGraw Hill, 2009), 593–94; Bennett et al., *The Cosmic Perspective* (2014), 388.

12. Jeffrey Bennett and Seth Shostak, *Life in the Universe*, 3rd ed. (San Francisco: Addison-Wesley, 2012), 382–83.

13. Guillermo Gonzalez and Jay W. Richards, *The Privileged Planet: How Our Place in the Cosmos is Designed for Discovery* (Washington, DC: Regnery, 2004), 151–167.

14. Bennett et al., *The Cosmic Perspective* (2014), 390.

15. Seeds and Backman, *Astronomy*, 272.

16. Hugh Ross, *The Creator and the Cosmos*, 3rd ed. (Colorado Springs: NavPress, 2011), 178.

17. Gonzalez and Richards, *The Privileged Planet*, 341.

18. Bennett and Shostak, *Life in the Universe*, 120–121.

19. Jonathan Lunine, *Earth: Evolution of a Habitable World*, 2nd ed. (New York: Cambridge University Press, 2013), 126; Comins and Kaufmann, *Discovering the Universe*, 141–142.

20. Carl B. Agee, "Hot Metal," *Nature* 429 (May 6, 2004): 33–35.

21. Bennett and Shostak, *Life in the Universe*, 121.

22. Bennett and Shostak, *Life in the Universe*, 196. The isotope ratio of carbon-13 to carbon-12 is slightly lower in samples containing the remnants of living organisms than in inorganic sample material.

23. Bennett et al., *The Cosmic Perspective* (2014), 205.

24. Bennett et al., *The Cosmic Perspective* (2014), 169–170; Charles Q. Choi, "How the Moon Formed: Violent Cosmic Crash Theory Gets Double Boost," Space.com, April 8, 2015, https://www.space.com/29047-how-moon-formed-earth-collision-theory.html.

25. Bennett et al., *The Cosmic Perspective* (2014), 197.

26. Seeds and Backman, *Astronomy*, 134; Lunine, *Earth: Evolution of a Habitable World*, 122.

27. Bennett and Shostak, *Life in the Universe*, 136–138.

28. Bennett et al., *The Cosmic Perspective* (2014), 220–222.

29. Lunine, *Earth: Evolution of a Habitable World*, 167–168.

30. Bennett et al., *The Cosmic Perspective* (2014), 222.

31. Bennett et al., *The Cosmic Perspective* (2017), 284.

32. Lunine, *Earth: Evolution of a Habitable World*, 241–242.

33. Sarah Fecht, "What Would Happen if Earth Started to Spin Faster?" *Popular Science*, May 17, 2017, https://www.popsci.com/earth-spin-faster/.

34. Along with a slowing of Earth's rotational rate, the average distance between the Earth and the moon is gradually increasing. Astronomers estimate that when the moon formed it was at least ten times closer to the Earth than it is now. Tidal interactions between the moon and the Earth have gradually transferred Earth's rotational energy to the moon. This interaction has the double effect of slowing the Earth's rotational rate and gradually pushing the moon away. Currently, the moon is receding from Earth at just under four cm per year. See Bennett and Shostak, *Life in the Universe*, 300.

35. V. S. Meadows and R. K. Barnes, "Factors Affecting Exoplanet Habitability," in *Handbook of Exoplanets*, eds. Hans J. Deeg and Juan Antonio Belmonte (New York: Springer, 2018), https://doi.org/10.1007/978-3-319-30648-3_57-1.

36. Hugh Ross, "Fine-Tuning for Life on Earth," "Probabilities for Life on Earth," and "Fine-Tuning for Life in the Universe," Reasons to Believe, November 16, 2010, https://reasons.org/explore/blogs/todays-new-reason-to-believe/read/tnrtb/2010/11/16/rtb-design-compendium-2009; also cited in Hugh Ross, *Why the Universe Is the Way It Is* (Grand Rapids, MI: Baker Books, 2008), 213–14.

37. David Waltham, *Lucky Planet: Why Earth is Exceptional—and What that Means for Life in the Universe* (New York: Basic Books, 2014), 2.

8. THE CRADLE OF LIFE (141–152)

1. Gerald L. Schroeder, *The Hidden Face of God: Science Reveals the Ultimate* Truth (New York: Touchstone, 2001), 48.

2. Jeffrey Bennett and Seth Shostak, *Life in the Universe*, 3rd ed. (San Francisco: Addison-Wesley, 2012), 196.

3. Bennett and Shostak, *Life in the Universe*, 7.

4. Jonathan Lunine, *Earth: Evolution of a Habitable World*, 2nd ed. (New York: Cambridge University Press, 2013), 125, 205.

5. Jeffrey Bennett et al., *The Cosmic Perspective: The Solar System*, 7th ed. (San Francisco: Pearson, 2014), 292.

6. Bennett et al., *The Cosmic Perspective* (2014), 336.

7. Fazale Rana and Hugh Ross, *Origins of Life*, (Colorado Springs: NavPress, 2004), 101.

8. Norio Kitadai and Shigenori Maruyama, "Origins of Building Blocks of Life: A Review," *Geoscience Frontiers* 9, no. 4 (2018): 1117–1153, https://doi.org/10.1016/j.gsf.2017.07.007.

9. Bennett et al., *The Cosmic Perspective* (2014), 704; Bennett and Shostak, *Life in the Universe*, 214.

10. Bennett et. al, *The Cosmic Perspective* (2014), 704.

11. Lunine, *Earth: Evolution of a Habitable World*, 211.

12. Lunine, *Earth: Evolution of a Habitable World*, 210.

13. Bennett and Shostak, *Life in the Universe*, 215.

14. Bennett and Shostak, *Life in the Universe*, 212.

15. Stephen C. Meyer, *Darwin's Doubt: The Explosive Origin of Animal Life and the Case for Intelligent Design* (New York: Harper One, 2013).

16. Lunine, *Earth: Evolution of a Habitable World*, 203-204.

17. Roger A. Hinrichs and Merlin Kleinbach, *Energy: Its Use and the Environment*, 5th ed. (Boston: Brooks/Cole, 2013), 277.

18. John D. Jackson, *Classical Electrodynamics*, 2nd ed. (New York: John Wiley & Sons, 1975), 290–291.

19. Lunine, *Earth: Evolution of a Habitable World*, 197–200.

20. Lunine, *Earth: Evolution of a Habitable* World, 200.

21. M. Ferus, et al., "Ariel—a Window to the Origin of Life on Early Earth?," *Experimental Astronomy* (2020), https://doi.org/10.1007/s10686-020-09681-w. For more on the Ariel mission, see Ariel Space Mission: European Space Agency M4 Mission, https://arielmission.space/.

22. Michael A. Seeds and Dana E. Backman, *Astronomy: The Solar System and Beyond*, 6th ed. (Belmont, CA: Brooks/Cole, 2010), 431, 434.

23. Paul Davies, *The Fifth Miracle: The Search for the Origin and Meaning of Life* (New York: Simon and Schuster, 1999), 87; Seeds and Backman, *Astronomy*, 434.

24. Fazale Rana, *Creating Life in the Lab: How New Discoveries in Synthetic Biology Make a Case for the Creator* (Ada, MI: Baker Books, 2011), 129.

25. Rana, *Creating Life in the Lab*, 180.

26. Eugene V. Koonin, "The Cosmological Model of Eternal Inflation and the Transition from Chance to Biological Evolution in the History of Life," *Biology Direct* 2 (2007): 8.

27. James Tour, "An Open Letter to My Colleagues," *Inference* 3, no. 2 (August 2017), https://inference-review.com/article/an-open-letter-to-my-colleagues.

28. Schroeder, *The Hidden Face of God*, 65.

29. Ed Yong, "Scientists Finish a 53-Year-Old Classic Experiment on the Origins of Life," *Discover*, March 21, 2011, https://www.discovermagazine.com/planet-earth/scientists-finish-a-53-year-old-classic-experiment-on-the-origins-of-life.

30. Davies, *The Fifth Miracle*, 90.

31. Tour, "An Open Letter to My Colleagues."

32. Stephen C. Meyer, *Signature in the Cell: DNA and the Evidence for Intelligent Design* (New York: HarperCollins, 2009), 236.

33. Davies, *The Fifth Miracle*, 107.

34. Davies, *The Fifth Miracle*, 92.

35. F. H. C. Crick and L. E. Orgel, "Directed Panspermia," *Icarus* 19 (1973): 341-346.

9. INFORMATION AND THE ORIGIN OF LIFE (153–176)

1. Early information theory did not emphasize this aspect. Later theorizing did. Kolmogorov complexity relates information content of a system to the shortest algorithm that can reproduce the sequence specifying the system. See, for example, Andrey Kolmogorov, "Logical Basis for Information Theory and Probability Theory," *IEEE Transactions on Information Theory* 14, no. 5 (September 1968): 662–664, doi:10.1109/TIT.1968.1054210.

2. Hubert Yockey, *Information Theory and Molecular Biology* (Cambridge: Cambridge University Press, 1992), 82.

3. R. Harald Baayen and Rochelle Lieber, "Word Frequency Distributions and Lexical Semantics," *Computers and the Humanities* 30 (1997): 281–291.

4. Arthur Hobson, *Concepts in Statistical Mechanics* (New York: Gordon and Breach Science Publishers, 1971), 139–140.

5. Hobson, *Concepts in Statistical Mechanics*, 142–145.

6. Paul Davies, *The Fifth Miracle: The Search for the Origin and Meaning of Life* (New York: Simon and Schuster, 1999), 57.

7. Jonathan Lunine, *Earth: Evolution of a Habitable World*, 2nd ed. (New York: Cambridge University Press, 2013), 151.

8. Hobson, *Concepts in Statistical Mechanics*, 143.

9. Charles Kittel, *Thermal Physics* (New York: John Wiley & Sons, 1969), 44–45.

10. Robert O'Connor, "The Design Inference: Old Wine in New Wineskins," in *God and Design: The Teleological Argument and Modern Science*, ed. Neil A. Manson (Abingdon: Routledge, 2003).

11. Hobson, *Concepts in Statistical Mechanics*, 153.

12. Brian Greene, *The Fabric of the Cosmos* (New York: Vintage Books, 2004), 175; Franklin M. Harold, *The Way of the Cell* (Oxford: Oxford University Press, 2001), 228–229.

13. Hugh D. Young and Roger A. Freedman, *University Physics*, 14th ed. (London: Pearson Education, 2016), 647.

14. Kolmogorov, "Logical Basis for Information Theory."

15. Douglas Axe, *Undeniable: How Biology Confirms Our Intuition That Life is Designed* (New York: Harper Collins, 2016). See also his peer-reviewed articles in the *Journal of Molecular Biology* describing laboratory results suggesting the practical impossibility of blindly evolving novel protein folds: "Extreme Functional Sensitivity to Conservative Amino Acid Changes on Enzyme Exteriors," *Journal of Molecular Biology* 301, no. 3 (August 2000): 585–595, https://doi.org/10.1006/jmbi.2000.3997 and "Estimating the Prevalence of Protein Sequences Adopting Functional Enzyme Folds," *Journal of Molecular Biology* 341, no. 5 (August 2004): 1295–1315, https://doi.org/10.1016/j.jmb.2004.06.058.

16. William A. Dembski, "Small Probability," chap. 6 in *The Design Inference: Eliminating Chance through Small Probabilities* (Cambridge, UK: Cambridge University Press, 1998).

17. This number can be approximated by using the estimate of one trillion galaxies in the universe, and one hundred billion stars per galaxy, and 10^{57} elementary particles (mostly protons, comprising hydrogen nuclei) in an average star.

18. Stephen C. Meyer, *Signature in the Cell: DNA and the Evidence for Intelligent Design* (New York: HarperCollins, 2009), 216–217. Meyer reproduces William Dembski's calculation for the maximum number of opportunities for an event to occur within the physical history of this universe, work presented in *The Design Inference*.

19. Meyer, *Signature in the Cell*, 212. Meyer is summarizing work by protein chemist Douglas Axe, published in the *Journal of Molecular Biology*, cited above. Meyer argues that the overall odds of producing one protein molecule composed of 150 amino acids is estimated by multiplying the probability of only incorporating peptide bonds ($1{:}10^{45}$) times the probability that each amino acid selected has the correct chirality ($1{:}10^{45}$), times the probability of getting the sequencing of 150 amino acids to result in a functional protein ($1{:}10^{74}$). The product of these three terms gives the overall probability as $1{:}10^{164}$.

20. Meyer, *Signature in the Cell*, 218.

21. Davies, *The Fifth Miracle*, 258–259.

22. Davies, *The Fifth Miracle*, 107; Gerald L. Schroeder, *The Hidden Face of God: Science Reveals the Ultimate Truth* (New York: Touchstone, 2001), 190.

23. Fred Hoyle and Chandra Wickramasinghe, *Evolution from Space* (London: Granada Publishing, 1981), 20. They estimated that a cell requires at least 2,000 proteins, and that the probability for a random amino acid sequence corresponding to a functional protein is 1 chance in 10^{20}. The probability of 2,000 amino acid sequences all corresponding to functional proteins is then 10^{20} to the power of 2,000, which is $10^{(20)(2000)}$. The resulting probability is $10^{40,000}$.

24. Richard Dawkins, *Climbing Mount Improbable* (New York: W. W. Norton & Company, 1997).

25. This many steps would be needed before a random search would have any chance of finding the target of a fully functional cell.

26. Due to thermal energy, atoms in solid material constantly undergo lattice vibrations at roughly a trillion oscillations per second, which gives a maximum interatomic interaction rate.

27. Harvey S. Leff and Andrew F. Rex, eds., *Maxwell's Demon: Entropy, Information, Computing* (Princeton, NJ: Princeton University Press, 1990); Robert Gange, *Origins and Destiny* (Waco, TX: World Books, 1986), 96–98.

10. DISCOVERING NATURE'S REACH (177–192)

1. Eric R. Hedin, Arkady M. Satanin, and Yong S. Joe, "Circular Transmission Resonances and Magnetic Field Effects in a Ring of Quantum Dots Connected to External Leads in the Meta-Configuration," *Journal of Computational Electronics* 18 (2019): 648–659, https://link.springer.com/article/10.1007/s10825-018-01291-2.

2. Stephen C. Meyer, *Darwin's Doubt: The Explosive Origin of Animal Life and the Case for Intelligent Design* (New York: Harper One, 2013); Michael Denton, *Evolution: Still a Theory in Crisis* (Seattle: Discovery Institute Press, 2016).

3. Niles Eldredge and Stephen Jay Gould, "Punctuated Equilibria: An Alternative to Phyletic Gradualism," in *Models in Paleobiology*, ed. Thomas J. M. Schopf (San Francisco: Freeman Cooper, 1972), 82–115. See also Stephen Jay Gould, *The Structure of Evolutionary Theory* (Cambridge, MA: Harvard University Press, 2002), chap. 9.

4. Rick Durrett and Deena Schmidt, "Waiting for Two Mutations: With Applications to Regulatory Sequence Evolution and the Limits of Darwinian Evolution," *Genetics* 180 (2008): 1501–1509.

5. Jonathan Wells, *Zombie Science: More Icons of Evolution* (Seattle: Discovery Institute Press, 2017), 113.

6. William A. Dembski and Jonathan Wells, *The Design of Life: Discovering Signs of Intelligence in Biological Systems* (Dallas: The Foundation for Thought and Ethics, 2008), 104.

7. Franklin M. Harold, *The Way of the Cell* (Oxford University Press, 2001), 205.

8. Alan H. Linton, "Scant Search for the Maker," Book Section, *Times Higher Education Supplement*, April 20, 2001, 20.

9. Michael J. Behe, *The Edge of Evolution: The Search for the Limits of Darwinism* (New York: Free Press, 2007).

10. Richard Dawkins, *The Blind Watchmaker*, 2nd ed. (New York: W.W. Norton, 1996), 1.

11. Francis Crick, *What Mad Pursuit: A Personal View of Scientific Discovery* (New York: Basic Books, 1990), 138.

12. Stephen J. Gould, *Punctuated Equilibrium* (New York: Belknap Press, 2007).

13. Meyer, *Darwin's Doubt*.

14. Stephen C. Meyer, "The Origin of Biological Information and the Higher Taxonomic Categories," *Proceedings of the Biological Society of Washington*, 117 (2004): 213–239.

15. This is an allusion to a documentary hosted by Ben Stein, *Expelled: No Intelligence Allowed* (2008). The film chronicles the experiences of Sternberg and several other scientists who were attacked and pushed out of their academic settings because they were willing to openly consider evidence from nature in support of intelligent design.

16. Michael Behe, *Darwin's Black Box: The Biochemical Challenge to Evolution*, 2nd ed. (New York: Free Press, 2006); Denton, *Evolution: Still a Theory in Crisis*.

17. Vitan Blagotinsek et al., "An ATP-Dependent Partner Switch Links Flagellar C-ring Assembly with Gene Expression," *PNAS* 117, no. 34 (August 25, 2020): 20826–20835, https://doi.org/10.1073/pnas.2006470117.

18. "NASA - STS-51L Mission Profile," NASA, December 5, 2005, http://www.nasa.gov/mission_pages/shuttle/shuttlemissions/archives/sts-51L.html; Karen Workman, "The Challenger Space Shuttle Disaster, 30 Years Later," *New York Times*, January 28, 2016, https://www.nytimes.com/interactive/2016/01/29/science/space/challenger-explosion-30-year-anniversary.html?_r=0.

19. Alvin Plantinga, *Where the Conflict Really Lies* (Oxford University Press, 2011), 315, and reference therein.

20. Charles Darwin to William Graham, July 3, 1881, Darwin Correspondence Project, University of Cambridge, https://www.darwinproject.ac.uk/letter/DCP-LETT-13230.xml.

21. Thomas Nagel, *Mind and Cosmos: Why the Materialist Neo-Darwinian Conception of Nature Is Almost Certainly False* (Oxford: Oxford University Press, 2012).

22. Plantinga, *Where the Conflict Really Lies*, 286.

23. Paul Davies, featured in *The Privileged Planet: The Search for Purpose in the Universe*, directed by Lad Allen (La Mirada, CA: Illustra Media, 2004), DVD.

24. Plantinga, *Where the Conflict Really Lies*, 350.

25. Plantinga, *Where the Conflict Really Lies*, 270.

26. One theological objection is that if our maker is so interested in our comprehending the underlying laws of the universe, why arrange things so that humanity had to wait long ages before the scientific revolution? But a Creator can have many purposes for his Creation, many gifts, and he isn't obligated to deliver all of them at once, or on the schedule of impatient humanity. In any case, what we find is a strikingly suitable match between our intellectual abilities and the level of challenge involved in making new discoveries about

nature, a match that makes sense on the grounds of theism, but remains inexplicable under philosophical naturalism.

27. Plantinga, *Where the Conflict Really Lies*, 217.

28. Plantinga, *Where the Conflict Really Lies*, 276.

29. Plantinga, *Where the Conflict Really Lies*, 266.

11. Mind, Beauty, and Information (193–208)

1. Wilder Penfield, *The Mystery of the Mind: A Critical Study of Consciousness and the Human Brain* (Princeton: Princeton University Press, 1975), 80.

2. Penfield, *The Mystery of the Mind*, 79-80.

3. Penfield, *The Mystery of the Mind*, 76.

4. Penfield, *The Mystery of the Mind*, 77.

5. G. K. Chesterton, *Orthodoxy* [1908] (Hollywood, FL: Simon & Brown, 2010), 28.

6. Chesterton, *Orthodoxy*, 28.

7. Chesterton, *Orthodoxy*, 29.

8. C. S. Lewis, *Miracles: A Preliminary Study* [1947] (New York: Harper Collins, 2001), 39.

9. Lewis, *Miracles*, 39.

10. Lewis, *Miracles*, 44.

11. Hans Urs von Balthasar, from the cover page of Thomas Dubay, S.M., *The Evidential Power of Beauty: Science and Theology Meet* (San Francisco: Ignatius Press, 1999).

12. Dubay, *The Evidential Power of Beauty*.

13. Dubay, *The Evidential Power of Beauty*, 36.

14. Dubay, *The Evidential Power of Beauty*, 42.

15. Dubay, *The Evidential Power of Beauty*, 39.

16. Alvin Plantinga, *Where the Conflict Really Lies* (Oxford: Oxford University Press, 2011), 297. The quality of hidden design, of something beyond the surface meaning or denotation, appeals strongly to our minds, something noted in a literary context by Oxford scholar C. S. Lewis. In his view, the stories we love best communicate not just a mechanistic plot, however well-woven, but an "atmosphere." And it is the experience of the atmosphere of such a story that draws one in, often to reread the story again and again. C. S. Lewis, "On Stories," in *On Stories and Other Essays on Literature* (Orlando, FL: Harcourt Books, 1982), as discussed in Michael Ward, *The Narnia Code: C. S. Lewis and the Secret of the Seven Heavens* (Carol Stream, IL: Tyndale House, 2010), 22–25.

17. Benjamin Wiker and Jonathan Witt, *A Meaningful World: How the Arts and Sciences Reveal the Genius of Nature* (Downers Grove, IL: InterVarsity Press, 2006), 28.

18. Wiker and Witt, *A Meaningful World*, 17.

19. Wiker and Witt, *A Meaningful World*, 171.

20. Wiker and Witt, *A Meaningful World*, 172.

21. Wiker and Witt, *A Meaningful World*, 250.

22. Wiker and Witt, *A Meaningful World*, 250.

23. Dubay, *The Evidential Power of Beauty*, 16.

24. Paul Davies, *The Mind of God: The Scientific Basis for a Rational World* (New York: Touchstone, 1992), 175.

25. G. H. Hardy, *A Mathematician's Apology* (Cambridge, UK: Cambridge University Press, 1940), 85.

26. Quoted by Frank Wiczek, "A Piece of Magic: The Dirac Equation," in *It Must be Beautiful*, ed. G. Farmelo (London: Granta Books, 2003), 123.

27. Eugene Wigner, "The Unreasonable Effectiveness of Mathematics in the Natural Sciences," *Communications in Pure and Applied Mathematics* 13, no. 1 (February 1960): 1–14.

28. William Pollard, "Rumors of Transcendence in Physics," *American Journal of Physics* 52, no. 10 (October 1984).

29. Lev Landau and Evgeny Lifschitz, *Course of Theoretical Physics*, vol. 2, *The Classical Theory of Fields*, 4th ed. (Oxford, UK: Butterworth-Heinemann, 1980), 245. S. Chandresekhar used the line in the title of "'The General Theory of Relativity: Why 'It is Probably the Most Beautiful of All Existing Theories,'" *Journal of Astrophysics and Astronomy* 5 (1984): 3–11.

30. Sabine Hossenfelder, *Lost in Math: How Beauty Leads Physics Astray* (New York: Basic Books, 2018).

31. Hossenfelder, *Lost in Math*, 38.

32. Hossenfelder, *Lost in Math*, 39.

33. Dubay, *The Evidential Power of Beauty*, 51.

34. Dubay, *The Evidential Power of Beauty*, 24. Dubay quotes the phrase "in its way absolutely perfect," from biochemist Lewis Thomas, "On the Uncertainty of Science," *Harvard Magazine* 83, no. 1 (1980):19–22.

35. Hans Urs von Balthasar, *The Glory of the Lord. A Theological Aesthetics*, vol. 1, *Seeing the Form* (San Francisco: Ignatius Press, 1982).

36. Martin Kemp, ed. *Leonardo on Painting: An Anthology of Writings by Leonardo da Vinci with a Selection of Documents Relating to His Career as an Artist*, trans. Martin Kemp and Margaret Walker (New Haven: Yale University Press, 1989), 32.

37. Richard Swinburne, *The Existence of God* (New York: Oxford University Press, 2004), 190.

38. A good introductory treatment of the theological problem of pain and evil in the world is C. S. Lewis, *The Problem of Pain* [1940] (San Francisco: HarperOne, 2001). For a more recent and extended treatment see Richard Swinburne, *Providence and the Problem of Evil* (Oxford: Oxford University Press, 1998).

39. Wiker and Witt, *A Meaningful World*, 65–69.

40. Lewis, *Miracles*, 94–95.

12. "WHAT A WORK" (209–224)

1. John A. Wheeler, "Information, Physics, Quantum: The Search for Links," in *Feynman and Computing*, ed. Anthony J. G. Hey (Boca Raton, FL: Taylor and Francis Group LLC, 2002), 109.

2. Stephen C. Meyer, *Signature in the Cell: DNA and the Evidence for Intelligent Design* (New York: HarperCollins, 2009), 394–395.

3. Psalm 19, Genesis 1.

4. John 1:1, 3a.

5. Anton Zeilinger, "Why the Quantum? It from Bit? A Participatory Universe?: Three Far-reaching, Visionary Questions from John Archibald Wheeler and How They Inspired a

Quantum Experimentalist," Metanexus, accessed January 16, 2021, https://metanexus. net/archive/ultimate_reality/zeilinger.pdf.

6. Roger Penrose, *The Road to Reality: A Complete Guide to the Laws of the Universe* (New York: Alfred A. Knopf, 2004), 706.

7. Robert Gange, *Origins and Destiny* (Dallas: Word Publishing, 1986), 164.

8. Some origins researchers propose that RNA molecules or autocatalytic reaction sets could have self-replicated before full cellular replication. The problem is that origins models based on such scenarios are entirely implausible, and even if RNAs or reaction sets could have self-replicated, they would have always moved away from life, never towards it. See Leslie E. Orgel, "The Implausibility of Metabolic Cycles on the Prebiotic Earth," *PLoS Biology* 6, no. 1 (2008): e18; James Tour, "Animadversions of a Synthetic Chemist," *Inference* 2, no. 2 (2016); Brian Miller, "On the Origins of Life," reply to Helen Hansma, Letters, *Inference* 5, no. 3 (2020).

9. Gange, *Origins and Destiny*, 90–91. [emphasis in original]

10. F. H Crick and L. E. Orgel, "Directed Panspermia," *Icarus* 19 (3): 341–346, 1973.

11. Franklin M. Harold, *The Way of the Cell* (New York: Oxford University Press, 2001), 99.

12. Rosalind Picard, "An MIT Professor Meets the Author of All Knowledge," *Christianity Today*, March 15, 2019, https://www.christianitytoday.com/ct/2019/april/rosalind-picard-mit-professor-meets-author-knowledge.html.

13. Eric R. Hedin, "Questions from the Edge: Using Informal Surveys to Build Rapport with Students," *Journal of College Science Teaching* (January/February 2007): 60–62.

14. Arthur Lovejoy, quoted in William W. Van Alstyne, "Academic Freedom and the First Amendment in the Supreme Court of the United States: An Unhurried Historical Review," *Law and Contemporary Problems* 53, no. 3 (1990): 79–154, http://scholarship.law.wm.edu/facpubs/748.

15. Hugh Ross, private communication.

16. Alexander W. Astin, Helen S. Astin, and Jennifer A. Lindholm, *Cultivating the Spirit: How College Can Enhance Students' Inner Lives* (San Francisco: Wiley, 2011), 1. [emphasis in original]

17. Astin, Astin, and Lindholm, *Cultivating the Spirit*, 7.

18. Harold, *The Way of the Cell*, 255.

19. Discovery Institute's Center for Science and Culture opposes any effort to require the teaching of intelligent design in public school science classrooms. They argue that such efforts politicize the scientific work of the intelligent design movement. They instead encourage a legally tested approach of exposing public high school biology students to peer-reviewed scientific evidence both for and against modern evolutionary theory, and thereby encouraging critical thinking skills and a deeper understanding of modern evolutionary theory. More on their science education policy can be found at "Discovery Institute's Science Education Policy," Discovery Institute, https://www.discovery.org/a/3164/.

20. Sarah Chaffee, "As Eric Hedin Earns Tenure, It's Time to Set the Record Straight—Again," Evolution News and Science Today, Discovery Institute, May 20, 2016, https://evolutionnews.org/2016/05/as_eric_hedin_e/.

21. Rice Broocks, *God's Not Dead: Evidence for God in an Age of Uncertainty* (Nashville: W Publishing, Thomas Nelson, 2013).

22. Job 19:25.

Acknowledgments

This book is distinct in a couple of crucial ways from the Boundaries of Science course I taught for six years in the Honors College at Ball State University, but there is significant overlap, and the attacks that came against the course from people outside the university (detailed in Chapter 1) provided the opportunity for me to share in these pages not just some big questions raised by modern scientific discoveries about humanity's place in the grand scheme of things, but also a story about intellectual freedom in the search for truth, ultimate meaning, and purpose. Rice Broocks, author of *God's Not Dead*, affirmed my desire to write this book and encouraged me by noting that the public attempts to cancel my course gave me a platform from which to share truths about the boundaries of science and the limits of natural processes.

I am grateful for so many people whose reviews and edits have contributed to improving my original manuscript. With each one's feedback, the quality of the book ratcheted upwards. This couldn't have happened by chance but only by the knowledgeable and wise input of scholars who shared their expertise to improve what I had written.

From the Discovery Institute, Casey Luskin and John West have provided guidance and counsel, not only for the book, but in the midst of the media storm surrounding the conflict over my course. Others who read an early version of the manuscript and helped to improve it were my colleagues from Ball State, Guillermo Gonzalez and David Ober. Conversations with Doug Axe and Brian Miller provided valuable feedback on information theory and the origin of life. Jonathan Witt's skillful editing for DI Press was like the work of sculptor carving off rough edges and shaping the manuscript into a polished form. I'm also indebted to the science reviewers, who have remained anonymous, but whose attention to detail has brought a further degree of accuracy and depth to the content.

Finally, I am eternally indebted to my wife and daughter, who have shared in every aspect of life with me, giving encouragement and standing with me through trials and blessings.

FIGURE CREDITS

FIGURE 3.1. Hubble's Law graph. "Hubble Plots." Image by Ivan Ramirez, 2017, Wikimedia Commons. CC-BY-4.0 license.

FIGURE 6.1. Planetary nebula. "The Helix Nebula: Unraveling at the Seams." Image by NASA/JPL, 2012. Used as permitted.

FIGURE 6.2. Relative abundance of the elements in the solar system. "Solar System Abundances." Image by 28Bytes, 2010, Wikimedia Commons. CC-BY-SA 3.0 license.

INDEX

CPSIA information can be obtained
at www.ICGtesting.com
Printed in the USA
FSHW010020180221